The Stinging

NEW WRITERS • NEW WRITING

Issue 45 | Volume Two | Winter 2021-22

'… God has specially appointed me to this city, so as though it were a large thoroughbred horse which because of its great size is inclined to be lazy and needs the stimulation of some stinging fly…'

—Plato, *The Last Days of Socrates*

The Stinging Fly
new writers, new writing

Editor: Danny Denton

Publisher
Declan Meade

Poetry Editor
Cal Doyle

Website Editor
Ian Maleney

Assistant Editor
Sara O'Rourke

Eagarthóir Filíochta
Aifric MacAodha

Editor-at-Large
Thomas Morris

Contributing Editors
Dan Bolger, Mia Gallagher, Lisa McInerney and Nidhi Zak / Aria Eipe

Printed by Walsh Colour Print, County Kerry

ISBN 978-1-906539-94-8 | ISSN 1393-5690

The Stinging Fly, PO Box 6016, Dublin 1 | info@stingingfly.org

The Stinging Fly is published twice a year by The Stinging Fly CLG.

The Stinging Fly CLG gratefully acknowledges the support it receives from
The Arts Council / An Chomhairle Ealaíon and the T.S. Eliot Foundation.

T. S. ELIOT FOUNDATION

NEW POEMS

COMHCHEALG

NEW ESSAYS

COVER ART

Róisín O'Sullivan

COVER DESIGN

Deirdre Breen

The Stinging Fly was established in 1997 to publish and promote the best new Irish and international writing. Published twice a year, we welcome submissions on a regular basis. Online submissions only. Please read the submission guidelines on our website.

Keep in touch: sign up to our email newsletter, become a fan on Facebook, or follow us on Twitter for regular updates about our publications, podcasts, workshops and events.

stingingfly.org | facebook.com/StingingFly | @stingingfly

Editorial

The editorial is always the last thing done when putting together issues of *The Stinging Fly*; is always written the day before we go to print, with a crammer's heartbeat and a time-to-clean-the-bathroom reluctance. I think it's because I don't want to say anything to steer readers, or to get in the way of the work speaking for itself. But we have these two pages here traditionally, and of course it does often end up (once the ink is flowing) feeling important to say something.

I've also always avoided singling out particular pieces in editorials, because you can't highlight every piece in the magazine (even though you've fallen in some sort of love with all of them); and if you can't single out everyone, single out no one, right? And yet certain work in this issue, for different reasons, feels important to single out this time. 'True Story', written anonymously, details a woman's experience of domestic abuse. I can't put into words all the things it makes me feel, and realise, but I think it's crucial that people read it. There can be understanding, power, escape, prevention and/or healing in reading testimonies like this, I hope.

In a very different but also crucial essay, Jessica Gaitán Johannesson's 'Freak Aguacero' deals with the climate crisis, and how we talk to our families about it. Climate *change* has of course already happened, and the climate crisis (or *emergency*) is here. It's happening around us right now. The world is burning, and increasingly drained of its resources. I don't know whether it's too late to save our planet, but it's certainly not too late to start trying. Jesse Ball says that when a poem is thrown at a window it should break the glass; I hope that essays like Gaitán Johannesson's and Anonymous's break the glass too.

Finally, for entirely different (and less stark) reasons, I want to highlight 'One Night Stands', a sequence for which we commissioned four writers to (separately) write a piece of short fiction in a single night. Read Thomas Morris's introduction to the sequence on page 15 for more. As editor of the magazine I've always tried to push writers in interesting directions—to remember that writing can be a form of exploration, or play. To remind ourselves, as writers, to be open and to go places that might not seem obvious (or easy). 'One Night Stands' epitomises that yearning for art to be joyful and a bit weird. For it to take us places we didn't expect to go. That, I think, is crucial too.

This reminds me of a story I've wedged into everything I've done: my teaching, my editing, my own first novel. It's an old Sufi parable that John Moriarty used to tell. This man walks home from work the same way every evening, up the same dark dark country road to his dark dark house on the edge of town. When he gets to the streetlight outside his house, he pulls his door key from his pocket and off in he goes for his evening's rest. But one evening, having walked up the dark dark country road, he gets to the streetlight, puts his hand in his pocket, and finds no key. He starts to search for the key, there in the pale glow cast by the streetlight, and ends up on his hands and knees scouring every inch of the lit road and pavement on the edge of town. A neighbour comes along and asks what he's up to, and when she hears his predicament begins to help. The two of them are searching for a while when she says, *Are you sure you lost it here?* And he says, *No, I lost it out there somewhere, in the dark.* And she says, *Well why in the name of Christ are we looking all round here then?* And he says, *Because this is where the light is.*

In our writing and our reading we should be ready and willing to push out into the dark, and to see or discover what's there. It's not always useful to look where we can already see well.

Like what Ben Marcus said about William Gaddis's work: 'I want to follow Gaddis wherever he goes, precisely because I've never been there before.'

Which reminds me of what Anne Carson said about thought: 'I don't know that we really think thoughts; we think connections between thoughts. That's where the mind moves, that's what's new, and the thoughts themselves have probably been there in my head for a long time. But the jumps between them are entirely of that moment. It's magical.'

Which makes me think of when David Lynch said: 'Movement is what creates the dream.'

And so this is another issue I've loved putting together—reading work that has moved my heart, my mind, my gut, but felt dreamlike all the same, turning my gaze outward, towards obscure country—and I'm so very proud to share the work with you. Thanks as always to my wonderful colleagues at *The Fly*, who keep the dream moving. Off we go now, out into the dark.

Danny Denton, November 2021

A short history of light

Butter light, starlight, hardly the softest light
falls thru skylight, pleasure light, telephone
light as a breeze light, pain light, the mail light
will melt on carpets & clock my light home
American light, gun light, lightest chrome
alone light, feather light, clear light, blue light
to permanent green light, gaslit sunlight
for Marlboro Light click this honeycomb
shop light, a house light, sempiternal gold
against pear light, red light, under the street
night halogen yellow, sultry light rung
as twilight back to your lover in cold
erotic blonde of good light, palest sheet
lightning inside you, really the same thing.

Maria Sledmere

Implosions (an excerpt)

Hyam Yared
translated from the French by Frank Wynne

August 4, 2020 at 6:07 pm—perhaps :08 or :09, accounts of the minutes vary—
the weather is glorious. I am alive. On all fours. On my knees. Thrown by the
blast. Floored. With my husband. And our couples therapist. Huddled under
her desk. Waiting for the third, the fourth, the fifth explosion.

Already, video footage is being relayed around the world. Mushroom
clouds, mountains of rubble, smashed cars, shattered windows.

It took only a split second: Beirut is no more than a shadow of what it was.

Our therapist, Nadine K, is bleeding from a gash on her forehead. I'm
scrabbling blindly for my glasses. Wassim, my husband, is asking after me
with unaccustomed solicitude.

'Are... are you... alright?'

'Yeah... yeah... I'm fine.'

A moment earlier he had been holding forth to Nadine K, explaining that
our marriage was on the rocks. Reeling off the list of flaws he blames on my
black moods. I interjected. Colours are clichés. There is nothing black about
the bleakness. He was insistent that bringing even a flicker of joy into my
heart was hard labour. 'Might as well try to bring peace to the Middle East. My
wife's nihilism would drive Sisyphus himself to drink. I mean, it's not exactly
sexy. You can't desire a bunch of dry twigs. She's volatile and unpredictable.
Her mood swings can shift in a zeptosecond.'

Nadine was giving him her best therapist's expression. He was determined
to have the last word.

'It's impossible to carry on a relationship in these circumstances. My wife's
constantly on edge, constantly stressed out. Anything and everything sets
her off. World affairs. Her new book being published. Thinking about writing
the next one. The future. The Lebanon. The whole fucking region. Our sex

9

life. Our parenting skills. Regional politics, the devaluation of the Lebanese pound, the high cost of living, the mounting national debt, the shifting tectonic plates of history—and don't get me started on the fact our skies are black with swarms of drones and planes, seagulls and mosquitoes.'

Nadine had been on the point of saying something when the explosion took us by surprise. I didn't have time to respond. Everything abruptly contracted only to dilate again—organs, veins, eye sockets, bodies, tensions, loves and rusty old grievances. Everything exploded into shards of glass and twisted metal. As for desire, that had long since been blown to pieces.

2

6:08 pm, Wassim spreads his arm like a stricken seagull's wing to shield me from the flying glass. Face pressed into the crook of his neck, I wish I felt a flicker of connection to what we once were. The slightest quiver at his touch. What if we could start over? 'Desire never dies,' my grandmother used to say. 'Keeping it alive is what stops us from losing our way.'

For months now, a listlessness had been gradually spreading through my skin. I had Beirut between my legs. Beneath a sky streaked by drones, bedsheets were no longer imbued with the perfumes of our bodies, our hair, of sexual organs drained from being overfilled, of all that remains of the midden of our beings. Not the minutest germ of desire—brutish, sensual or literary—kindled between the four walls of our bedroom.

At some point during the death throes of the October thawrat, the economic crisis and the pandemic, our marriage had begun to fall apart. Now that Wassim was working from home, he never bothered to change out of his tracksuit, while I schlepped around in slippers and a hideous velour onesie. Two passion-killers under the same roof. We stared at each other, hopeless, helpless, unable to remember the most basic gestures that might ignite the deadwood of our bodies. Nothing sparked. Not the slightest urge—sexual, asexual, cerebral or creative. To stoke the flames of passion, you need to feel that you exist, just as, in order to inhabit its borders, a country needs to feel that it exists. If only a little. An iota. No strength to reawaken an ember. No desire to live or to write. To experience a moment of joy, or even carnal pleasure. A carefree moment.

As the world lurches from crisis to crisis, it has become clear that not everyone gets to live in a lambda country. 'What's a lambda country?' asked Asma, the second youngest of our five girls. Lambda countries have been spared the horrors of war for so long that their people have forgotten what it means to suffer, I told her. The Lebanon isn't a lambda country. Here, our passions tear us apart, they urge us on to empathise or to kill. To give way to violence or to help our neighbour. To allow ourselves to be moved by the tenderness buried beneath the ashes. Chasms filled to the brim with profound solace like an abyss in which there is nothing. Nothing but that last trace of humanity—good or bad—that springs from the very contradictions that the 'rich' world seems to have forgotten.

Here, we trudge through survival, united by tragedy, yet always on the point of giving up, on partners, families, neighbours; here in the Lebanon we know what it means to muddle through. Broken yet soldered together, a country always on the point of imploding that somehow endures. Like our marriage. I don't explicitly make this connection. Not that it matters, since Asma is all too familiar with the nights when our angry voices drown out the roar of the planes. Not that this stops us smiling when morning comes. Nothing can stop us. Lovers can't afford to fight in a country ravaged by war. Sheer survival takes precedence over divorce, and compassion is reborn from the ashes of the inevitable: the need to build a future in spite of everything.

3

6:09 pm. Wassim and I are on all fours, like a pair of fighting bulls. Seen from below, couples therapy looks very different. The pecking order, the couple, the family tree, the therapist. Eight months earlier, we had been forced to deal with the sudden departure of Nadine K's colleague, the original counsellor tasked with repairing our marriage. Overcome by the tragedies that plagued the country, she had given up. She no longer had the strength to carry on. The countless national crises—security, health, political and economic—had proved too much. There are advantages to dual citizenship. She had it. So the decision to stay or to leave was easy. By way of goodbye, she simply texted all her clients: 'Sorry, I'm taking my Labradors and going to live with my sister in Greece. I won't be back. These are dangerous times and the Lebanon is doomed.'

Nadine's scream drills in my ears. Her eyes bore into me. The expression on her face, ordinarily so calm and poised, is that of a hunted animal. Suicide attacks, mortar fire, shelters, bombing raids—these things are new to her. She was spared the horrors of war by her parents, who fled to Europe at the first signs of hostility back in 1975; her entire sense of the Lebanon is rooted in a sepia-tinged nostalgia and a longing to return to an imagined country, which—alone of her three siblings—she finally assuaged when, in 2018, she moved to Beirut.

Fifteen kilometres as the crow flies from the blast, the wellness clinic is quaking. Nadine is shrieking, her hands clapped over her ears to silence the sound of this war her parents implicitly used to justify leaving the country as soon as the first clashes broke out.

'This... this... this is my first explosion!'

I envy her this spluttering terror. Self-control is ingrained in me like a rancid memory. I'd love to be able to act instinctively. To give in to panic. To be unfamiliar with verminous fears. Extricating myself from my husband's embrace, I put my arms around her. She in the lotus position, me on my knees. My husband is already heading for the door.

'Quick! Out into the corridor!'

Living in certain countries requires skills that range from basic first aid to an advanced understanding of structural engineering and the ability to pinpoint the safest refuge during a bombing. It is folk wisdom, a lullaby passed down to us by our parents: 'When you hear an explosion, get away from the windows and head for a room that doesn't overlook the street. Wait for the second explosion, then run to the bomb shelter. It's while you're running from A to B that death surprises you!'

4

In crocodile formation, we follow Wassim, oblivious to what is happening outside. Right now, survival is a matter of arses. Wassim's is almost pressed against Nadine's face, hers is against mine, mine exposed to the air. We crawl, oblivious to the splinters of glass crackling beneath our palms. I am poleaxed by a brutal spasm. A bout of flatulence due to stress or maybe asthma—for months now, various specialists have offered contradictory opinions. My gastroenterologist insists it's due to stress, my pulmonologist is equally insistent that it's asthma-related aerophagia. I freeze, paralysed by cramp. I feel my heart accelerate, I can hear it pounding in my temples, hammering against my ribs. Blood coursing through me like molten lava. The pulmonologist recommended yoga to control my breathing. I inhale. I exhale. Until the spasm passes.

In the corridor, I catch up with Nadine. She and Wassim have just reached the windowless toilets in the centre of the clinic. The cut on Nadine's forehead is a superficial graze, but the sight of blood is enough to make me forget my bout of colic. Suddenly, I think about our youngest daughters, jump to my feet, retrace my steps, hopping over rubble to retrieve my phone. The screen is cracked, but I manage to get through to Gilberte, the nanny we hired in a fit of panic when I was seven months pregnant with the twins. Having had three daughters in my twenties by my first husband, the thought of being stuck at home, alone, at forty, with two new-borns, is terrifying. This, according to the 2018 Agence France-Presse report, makes me a 'polluter', because if every woman had one less child, her carbon footprint would be drastically reduced. A factoid I mentioned to Nadine during one of our sessions. Wassim—who always has a pat response—said 'Easy—just stop travelling so much.' He's convinced every trip inflicts a gaping wound on our Little Poppet. Mothers, he believes, are irreplaceable.

The crowd next to the clinic's toilets begins to swell as the treatment rooms disgorge three physios, a speech therapist, two psychiatrists and their patients. By the time I first met Wassim, I had long given up on finding someone else. After my first marriage, there had been many false starts before I finally stopped shovelling my hopes and my trust into the bottomless pit of relationships. One former lover had ghosted me when he discovered I wasn't prepared to meekly play the role of the little woman who allows herself to be subtly humiliated. I had been the one to walk out, but I thought that he would come after me. Instead, I got a break-up email. Another had taken to his heels as soon as he realised that I already had three teenage daughters. And yet, when I met Wassim, I had not had doubts. I had seen only him, his hands, his smile, his sunny disposition. He is one of those people you instantly knew had had a happy childhood and was determined to give back what he was given. He reeled me in with words. Found the right things to say. I had given up meeting anyone when I heard him say, 'I've spent forty-three years waiting to find you...'

He plunged his eyes deep into mine, merged his life with mine. *If I have survived loving you/it is because there are embers still/from my auto-da-fé*, I wrote to him in blank verse. *In our throats the sky is liquid pure.* He simply stared at me, blankly. Later, I discovered that this was his standard reaction to literature. I was his first poet. For my part, I was reassured by his words, so firmly rooted in the real. We allowed ourselves to hide within each other, like a couple of teenagers nostalgic for something we felt we had lost. Love did the rest. I sank into a loving coma that all but made me forget about literature, about writing. At least for a time. Until language returned and whipped me like a gust of wind.

ONE NIGHT STANDS

Written by	Jon McGregor
	Rebecca Ivory
	Stephen Sexton
	Marie-Helene Bertino

Curated by	Thomas Morris

An introduction

We asked four authors to write a short piece of fiction in a single night: starting at dusk, and submitting by dawn. The idea began with Danny Denton and I thinking about Franz Kafka's 'The Judgment', which Kafka claimed to have written in a single night. (Cathy Sweeney's essay on the story, published in Issue 44, prompted our chat.)

The last few years, writing fiction has scared the shit out of me. I have been afraid to just sit down and write a story. Instead, I've taken refuge in what I thought was editing, but was actually a fearful kind of second-guessing and compulsive ruminating. Unchecked, 'editing' became for me a chronic defence-mechanism, a knotted means of avoiding the essential creative encounter with Not-Knowing.

So in an act of projection, I wondered: what would happen if writers were forced to not over-think, to not over-knead the dough, to just write a story straight through? I emailed four authors and asked: 'If we supply a prompt, will you write us a story in a night?' In retrospect, I am both surprised and not-surprised that they all agreed to give it a go.

At 7pm on the agreed evenings, I sent the authors the following instructions:

*We want you to write a piece of fiction (2500 words, approx) that includes **at least four** of these five words:*

bed   **buried**   **velvet**   **river**   **father**

You are welcome to pluralise or change the tense/form of the words (e.g. rivers, burying). There will be an opportunity for a light copyedit (fixing up typos, etc), but nothing substantive can change from first draft. Your deadline is 7am tomorrow.

Up until this point, the authors had no idea what form the prompt would take. Danny and I liked the idea that they'd each receive the same five words. We wondered: where would these words take them? By what logic would they seek to connect the words? Which words would they choose to omit? Using all the same ingredients, how different, how similar, would their dishes taste?

To find these five words, I invited Cathy Sweeney to flick through her pages of 'The Judgment' and drop her finger on random points and tell us where it landed. I then asked Danny Denton to name the images that came to his mind when he thought of 'The Judgment'. I chose two words from each of Cathy and Danny's selections: *bed, buried, river, father*—then I just felt we needed one more word, a word from outside of the world of Kafka's story. I hummed and hawed for a suitable method, but in the end I just chose the word on the tip of my tongue. I didn't overthink it.

Thomas Morris, Editor-at-Large

Dwell

Jon McGregor

written 30th September 2021

We buried my father in the dry river bed, with fires on the horizon and engines turning over in the deep velvet distance of the coming night.

We'd been walking in the river bed for hours, following its wend and weave while stooping low and taking turns to haul the trailer behind us. We no longer knew if there was anyone to be stooping out of sight from but we were taking no chances. Clark said I should stick my head up and see, and when I told him he should stick his head up his arse and see *that* my father told us to for God's sake stop fighting and focus. His voice was very quiet by then. I had to lower my ear to his mouth and ask him to repeat what he'd said. There was a huge effort in him drawing enough breath to speak. I watched the jerk and heave of his chest. I told Clark my father had said to knock off being such a prick, and all three of us were quiet for a while. The river wasn't totally dry. There was a muddy trickle running down the middle, and in some places slick patches of shallow mud. There was a faint reek of dead fish, and a kind of seaweed tang. I didn't know how far we were from the coast, or what the plan might be when we got there. The roar of the fires in the town and the ash falling from the sky and the occasional passing truck along the road made it difficult to think. My father on the trailer was heavy and the going was slow. Each time we hit a rock or rut he would wince and cry out. We had to give him a handkerchief to bite on to stifle his cries, as small as they were.

I don't think I can get there, he said, before taking the handkerchief. I think we need a different plan. I don't know what to suggest.

I looked at him. He didn't say: Leave me here. He didn't say: You go on without me. Save yourselves. He said: It really bloody hurts, can you watch the bumps? He said: Sean, why did you have to go and open the door? He said, slowly: is it still bleeding?

Clark, I said. Clark, check the dressing. Should we change the dressing? Is it tight enough? Have we staunched the bleeding?

Clark said: Staunched? The fuck you mean, staunched? You check it, I'm not a doctor.

I said, Clark, please, just help me out here, how's it looking?

Clark muttered something, cleaned his hands with a wet-wipe from the go-bag, and started picking at the soaked layers of the dressing. My father looked at me as the layers were pulled back. There were sticky sounds of unpeeling, and with each rasp my father pinched his lips together and closed his eyes. Clark was swearing under his breath, and then he went very quiet. My father's eyes widened suddenly, and lost focus. I couldn't remember when I'd last looked at him like this. For the last few months we'd been living in very close proximity but our communication had been functional and terse. Pass me this. Have you got that. Watch the street. Your turn to sleep. Check the firing pin. And before this all started we'd had no particular need to talk at all. I would no more have sat face to face with him than I would have sat face to face with a clock. His skin was smoother than I'd come to imagine. He had the wrinkles of his age but between them the skin was smooth. It looked soft, although I didn't touch it. There was a flush in his cheeks that looked almost youthful. I'd never thought of him as a man who would moisturise. It was difficult to imagine he'd been finding the time. He came back into focus and looked at me deeply. He nodded. I didn't know what he meant. It could have meant anything. Clark finished redoing the dressing, and my father's whole body jerked as he pulled the last layer tight. He stood up, and as he did so he leaned towards me and muttered: he's fucking fucked, mate. My father nodded at me again, and with a faint smile, he said: Sean, why did you have to go and open the door?

She had been out there all afternoon. It didn't add up. I knew something was wrong. I should have known something was wrong. But I kept watching. She was moving carefully, keeping low behind the burnt-out cars. She passed down the street three times over several hours. She was good, but she wasn't invisible.

The fuck is she doing, Clark whispered, as we watched from the top window. She looked like she had no plan, which was a bad sign. I knew her from school, from before, but Clark said he didn't remember her.

Yeah you do, I said. Lynsey Jones. Top class for everything. Always had a lead role in the school play. Hung out with the Hannahs, mostly. Duncan said he went all the way with her at Filby's party but no one believed him. A look of remembering came over Clark's face.

That Lynsey Jones? She had long hair then, right? Ginger?

I said I thought it was auburn but never mind.

He said: Lynsey Jones? As though saying her name again would help him to recover the memory, the full memory not just of her but of school days, before, with everyone wearing clean clothes and leaving food on their plates at lunch-time and getting into arguments with the teachers about homework or getting into fights in the corridor without understanding what it meant to actually hurt anyone, and maybe he was remembering, also, that after school we would walk home in great noisy crowds, walk down the middle of the road, shouting, standing up straight, bundling into shops to buy or steal armfuls of sweets and salty snacks and fizzy drinks, or going for chips, or standing around for just basically ever, like the sun was never going to stop shining and none of us needed to be anywhere and no one was going to hijack food trucks or blockade roads or burn the empty warehouses to the ground. He was remembering, possibly, that I'd once told him it had actually been me who had stood out at the end of Filby's garden with Lynsey, the night of the party, the music and chatter from the house far behind us and the moment softly blurring as we both leaned towards each other. Not that I'd told him the rest of it: how soft her lips were, or that she'd tasted of bubblegum and cider, or that the way her fingers played with my fingers was more thrilling somehow than the actual kiss and the hot feeling fizzing up through my chest. Not that I'd told anyone, or that she'd seemed to remember any of it the next time I'd seen her.

Lynsey *fucking* Jones, Clark said, a third time, like he was actually trying to attract her attention, and this time she looked up at us, straight at us, and we dropped to the floor but there was no doubt we'd been seen.

Fuck sake, Clark whispered, and that was about right. We didn't tell my father, and we stayed out of sight, and the next time we dared look she was gone. We heard a truck drive past and then nothing. It had been a while since we'd seen trouble. Most of the houses in the street were burnt through, and we'd made sure ours also looked abandoned. The trouble had mostly moved on. But my father had kept saying we weren't to let down our guard. We're a long way from letting our guards down, lads, he said.

My father had a lot of advice. He acted like he knew what he was doing; like this was something he'd been through before. Make your decisions and keep moving, lads. Stay out of the sun. Keep someone on watch at all times. Acknowledge what's happened but don't dwell. You've seen what happens to the ones who dwell. He said that to Clark when we first found him in the yard behind the Mistrys' house. Know your exit routes. Keep your go-bag ready. Once, cornered in the loading bay at the supermarket and waiting for the right moment to fight clear, he passed me a water bottle and told me to stay hydrated. Stay *hydrated*? I repeated. An explosion went off by the doors, so there was no time to dwell, but later it became a joke between us. Stay hydrated, I would say to Clark, when we broke cover during a raid, or when the trucks appeared in the night. Stay hydrated, he would mutter, when my father stepped out to negotiate.

Clark never told us what had happened at the Mistrys' house, but I gathered he'd lost the last of his family there. My father told him not to dwell, and he didn't. He didn't ask me what had happened to Brian, who took a wrong turn when we were on the other side of town, early on, or about my mum, who had basically just never come home. It was taken for granted that things had happened. Things had kept happening, and when we thought it would surely be over things had just kept falling apart. The important thing was not to dwell.

I was on watch when Lynsey came to the door. Clark and my father were eating upstairs. I watched through the hatch as she stood there and knocked. I looked through the other hatches and the whole street was clear.

Sean, please, I need your help, she said, softly.

She was pressed right against the door frame, keeping as narrow a profile as she could. Her face was turned to the street but she directed her words straight at me. Her hair was hacked close to her scalp.

Sean, I know you're there. Sean, you're the only one I can trust. Please.

None of it made any sense. Even the sound of someone knocking was like a sound from before. I told her I'd open but she had to come in quickly. She didn't turn around but I could see her shoulders relax the way they used to when she smiled in class. I slid back the bolts and inched the door open, and as soon as she turned I saw my mistake.

Sean, she said again, as the others came into view: I'm sorry.

When it was over we waited until dark and then left. We already had our go-bags but my father said there was more we should take. From the hold. We had to break down a false wall to get to it. There were blankets and tins and dried goods and medicines. Clark was more than a little surprised.

The fuck, Mr Jackson, he said. Were you saving this for a rainy day?

There was some discussion about whether to take it. If we're found with all this they'll finish us, Clark said.

And if we don't take it we won't get far, my father replied. Not far enough. His words were coming in snatches of wet breath by then. He was leaning against the kitchen counter, pushing the first dressing pack hard into the wound.

We'll need enough to. Make the coast.

What does he mean, the coast? Clark asked me.

Where the sea meets the land? I told him. Waves crashing on the beach? Ice-cream van, rubber dinghy, maybe a lighthouse?

Fuck off, Clark said, and started loading the trailer. My father tried to say more: People, at the coast. My. People.

Your people, I asked him: like who? Who? No one had people anymore. I didn't know what he meant. He'd stopped talking, leaning hard into the pain. When we left I bolted the door from the inside and climbed out of the window, so that if they came back they wouldn't know straight away we were gone. If they came after us we'd be too slow. We moved through the back alleys and we listened for trucks and we worked our way out of town. My father was still on his feet at that point, but you could barely call it walking. He was bent out of shape and staggering. It was like trying to get home with a drunk. Twice Clark said: Mr Jackson, I'm sorry, are you sure you can manage? And twice my father said: yes, bear with me, I'll be right in a mo. We stopped when we heard gunfire several streets away, and waited for the trucks to disperse. I was trying not to think too far ahead. When we came to the scrubland outside town I could already see dawn in the distance and I knew we were moving too slow. My father stopped and sank down onto the loaded trailer, the air leaking out of him slowly, and it was the first time he'd sat since the knife had gone in. There was relief in his eyes but also a kind of woozy delusion. Oh, that's better, he said. I think. I'm coming out the other. The side. The other side now, boys. Give me. Give me a minute. I'll be. Right. Right as rain. In a. In a jiffy. Jiffy! The word *jiffy* made him snuffle with laughter, and he lay back on the trailer. Give me a jiffy, he said, quietly. Clark had loaded the trailer with the tins and dried goods at the bottom and the blankets folded on top. It was like he'd already thought this through. He loosened the webbing and laid it over my father, and together we strapped him down tight. Let's fucking go, Clark said, and we headed towards the river. Behind us in the town there were explosions, and more buildings started to burn.

Ours was the last house on the street. We should have known they'd come for us. They only wanted the supplies, but things became unreasonably heated. My father came into the room last, unexpectedly, and there was a reaction. There were four of them with her, but it was Lynsey who put in the knife. She glanced at me for a second, with surprise in her eyes. She cupped her hand to the back of my father's head, bracing his weight as she slipped the knife gently out again. She told the others it was time to go, and they moved quickly, carrying the last of our food out to the truck. I thought she might say something once they were gone. Another apology, or something to acknowledge we were once friends. But she followed them outside and closed the door behind her, and we were left with my father pouring blood across the floor. He had a smile on his face like a victory, and I knew he was thinking of the supplies he'd hidden behind the false wall.

We buried my father in the dry river bed, with fires on the horizon and engines turning over in the deep velvet distance of the coming night.

The digging was hard. We had only a small trowel between us, and we took turns while the other kept watch. There was mud and gravel but we kept hitting rocks that needed levering out of the way. It was hard but there was a satisfaction. The task was clear and there was progress in it. I worked quickly and built up a sweat that cooled quickly in the settling night. Clark put a hand on my shoulder and gestured that he'd take a turn.

Stay hydrated, he whispered, and I told him to fuck off. I went back to my father and made sure he was comfortable. We'd left the trailer as far back as seemed sensible, but the sound of the digging was still loud. The trowel striking into the gravelled mud, and Clark's stifled grunts as he dug. My father looked at me from a long way off. His eyes were clear but I didn't know what he could see. He nodded again. His breathing was shallow and slow. There were great gaps when he didn't seem to be breathing at all. Each time he looked as though he would speak he could only move his lips slightly and then nod. His skin was drawing back against the bones of his face. His face was terribly cold. I could hear trucks again in the distance, but they were still a long way off. There was a glow of fire away to the north. I thought it was north. The river was heading generally east to the coast, but the wend and weave of it meant there was no real way of knowing north where we were. I wondered why I kept saying wend and weave. I listened to the steady rasp of Clark's digging. The boy knew how to maintain a pace. I listened to the whisper of my father's breath. I closed my eyes for a moment and settled into something like sleep. I thought of how quiet it had been at the end of the garden, at Filby's party that night. Deep in the shadows between the trees. The music from the house and everyone shouting, and the way those sounds didn't quite reach. The softness of Lynsey's kisses. The way the moment had seemed to stretch out. The abundance of it. Her hands. I thought of the word abundance. The hours of the school day, the noise of us, and the hours of wandering around after school. The way the doors of the supermarket would slide open in welcome as we moved towards them. The cool air inside like a kiss. The shelves so full they had to pile extra produce at the aisle ends, and keep rolling in more from the towering storage racks out the back. The word aisle, like a church. The first time I'd seen empty shelves at the supermarket, and how brazen and wrong it had seemed. The way Lynsey had thumbed into the gaps between my fingers, and the surge of suggestion she pushed into me. The first time I'd seen people fighting in the supermarket, pulling packets from each other's trollies and forcing their way to the checkouts to pay. The first time I saw people simply pick up what they could and push past the security guards at the door. The first time I saw security guards carrying guns. The first time I saw security guards die. The way Lynsey had put her flat hand to my shoulder when we finished kissing and said, with a smile, shall we go back inside. The plummeting feeling I was left with when I said okay. The way my father had said, once Mum hadn't come back for three days: well, okay, so she's gone. Or when Brian had taken the wrong turn: there's nothing we can do. Keep moving. The way Lynsey had cupped the back of my father's head, so gently, as though she was about to kiss the side of his gasping face.

*

We buried the river and my father stayed with us, deep into the velvet bed of dusk.

We rivered my father in the buried dusk, and the dry bed was velvet beneath our hands.

We fathered the dusk and my river was velvet, deep in the buried night.

We acknowledged what had happened, and moved on quickly towards the coast. We didn't dwell.

Arrivals

Rebecca Ivory

written 1st October 2021

I don't hear anything for three days and then on Tuesday night at the end of my shift at the restaurant, Dan leaves me two WhatsApp voice notes. One is four and a half minutes long and the next is a little over two minutes. He also sends three messages on Instagram (two *Reductress* headlines and a meme about old people on Facebook). It's almost midnight for me, so seven in the evening for him. I play his voice note while cycling home:

'I have had a *truly* awful day,' he begins. He has been living in New York for seven months and now uses *truly* an unnatural amount in conversation. I think he's picked this up from his American friends. But who am I to talk? Until recently I was certain that *amn't* was a real word and I often say *pacifically* instead of *specifically*. Anyway, I am too critical of people who adopt the accent of the country that they're temporarily living in, as if it isn't normal or healthy for people to change depending on who they spend time with. I start the voice note from the beginning because I wasn't actually listening, my mind had wandered:

'I have had a *truly* awful day. This morning, I was on the train and a couple started a flash mob—actually, maybe it wasn't a flash mob, there was only the two of them, swinging around the poles and twirling along the carriage—but anyway, they caused this huge distraction and everyone was clapping and cheering and I just wanted to listen to 'Picture of You' by Boyzone but couldn't hear it over the commotion. Then I started to think how great it would be if *I* could dance and if people clapped for *me*. So, then I had this fantasy about me competing in one of those *Strictly Come Dancing* charity shows. You know the ones that the local GAA clubs organise as their annual fundraiser? And that's a pathetic ambition but I'm too old to ever be a real dancer so I have to adjust my fantasies to meet my current potential. Because, what's the point in a fantasy if there's no hope it will ever materialise?'

I let out a sloppy laugh which must seem unbidden to the young couple I cycle past in the dark. I feel bad, I don't have a bike light and I'm sure that's annoying for drivers and pedestrians. My boyfriend James thinks I replaced my broken light weeks ago but I keep forgetting and it's a weird lie that I keep telling because I'm embarrassed that I can't reliably complete simple tasks. There are still several minutes of Dan's voice note left:

'Also, I met Pete on my lunch break and I don't know what's going on there. I told him how upset I was that he ignored me for a week and that I couldn't be with someone who thought that was acceptable behaviour. Of course, I didn't expect him to *agree*. He said that he didn't think we should keep seeing each other because he didn't want to hurt me because he cared about me. Obviously, I started to back track then because I was only trying to scare him and the last thing I wanted was for him to call my bluff. And he was so *sad*, saying he had felt really good about us so then I felt like I had made a *huge* mistake and was almost crying on my way back to the office. But listen, an hour later he texted to say he didn't think he could stop seeing me and invited me to his apartment tonight? So, honestly, I'd say he's full of shit but I'm still really attracted to him so I probably will have sex with him later.'

In the second voice note, he says he got a new job. He doesn't say exactly what it is but it must be decent if he quit his job as studio assistant in Bushwick. In the final minute of his message, he says that he'll have two weeks off before he starts and he's decided to visit home this weekend. I stop listening and start recording a reply: 'How long exactly are you home for? How much time will we get together?'

I still have a bell on my bike, and ring it three, four, five times, in excitement, and stand up to pedal faster because as well as missing a light, my bike has only one gear.

James is still up when I get home. Dan and I moved into this house when we started in NCAD together, seven years ago. After Dan left, James moved in with me. The house belongs to Dan's great-aunt. She lives in a nursing home. We pay a tiny amount of rent to Dan's father. In return, we have to preserve the décor which includes a lot of framed Sacred Hearts and images of baby

Christ and tiny mounted figures depicting his waxy, flushed face and thick lashes as he hangs on the cross, dying. I love it because I'm in the middle of a Masters in Fine Art and find these knick-knacks an endless source of inspiration for my projects. It's no different to collecting vintage teacups but James doesn't like it. He's Protestant although he says it's nothing to do with that, he's asthmatic and these items gather a lot of dust.

James is watching *The Sopranos* when I get home. He abruptly turns off the TV because he's not supposed to watch ahead without me. I lean down and hug him around his neck.

'Colleen, you stink of garlic mayonnaise, it's turning my stomach,' he says, shaking me off.

'Dan is coming home next week!' I do a little can-can dance and clap my hands under my leg as it flies mid-air.

'Next week?' James asks, trying to grab my leg.

'Yeah, on Sunday, actually,' I tell him. 'I might see if he wants to stay here for a couple nights.'

'Right, absolutely. It's his house. I might stay with Noel while he's here, though,' he says.

James and Dan are wary of each other which is nice for me, I can always complain about one to the other. The only time it has bubbled over into outright animosity was at our graduation when James wore a pink velvet jacket with black silk lining. Dan asked James, in front of my parents, if he also smoked one of those novelty bubble-pipes and shortly afterwards, James slipped the coat off. I think the fact that he paid nearly three hundred euro for it made it worse for him.

I sit on the kitchen counter and text Dan: Will you stay with me next week? James won't be around.

James is still talking and then saying: 'Colleen, Colleen, Colleen,' in a monotone voice until I shout at him to stop. Dan replies: Offended you felt the need to ask. Obviously, I will be staying with you. I lived there first. James accuses me of not listening to him until I insist that I *am* listening, and ask can he just repeat the last bit.

On Wednesday, I have class all day. After finishing my degree, I worked for two years in a tiny gallery before deciding to go back for my Masters. I only did this because Dan had found a job in New York, a revelation which made me feel betrayed: I had thought we were both supposed to be flailing, stumbling and floundering our way through together? I had known he was more talented than me but I didn't think he cared about that. So, I panicked and now I owe the Credit Union eight thousand euros. My class is arranging an exhibition of all our work for January. My classmate, Nathaniel, is especially versatile and if he were a woman, I'd feel threatened by this. He makes art about Climate Change and the futility of our efforts to mitigate its effects. He created an artificial river in a block of concrete and will invite participants to deposit their litter in the river, until it chokes the flow and cuts off the water. Nathaniel is also the best in our class at digital design. I'm struggling with Adobe Illustrator so I ask him to help me after class. James is a graphic designer so I could go to him but I don't because I like spending time with Nathaniel.

'Oh yeah, I see what you've done wrong, you've tried to place this image as a jpeg but you should load it in Photoshop first, then resize it,' he tells me, after I present him with a problem I could have Googled. He could have told me to Google it, but he didn't.

I don't know when I got so fickle. I think it's because I don't believe I'm attractive. So even if James likes how I look, it's not enough reassurance. At an initial glance, I have a well-proportioned body and nice red hair. But my eyes are a little too close together and my nose is small and round and my fulcrum is a little too long so I sometimes think I look like a gnome. And my neck is too short, Dan always says this. It's terrible for a woman to have no neck, it just is.

Nathaniel walks up Thomas Street with me, until I get to work. He says he's invited to speak at the National Gallery about a piece of his they've selected for a themed exhibition. I ask him questions and hardly listen to the answers, focusing too much on the next piece of insight I can offer. He's talking to me about the end of the world, how it's already happening and that we shouldn't really think of it as one final event but as a series of increasingly devastating disasters. He's not looking at me as I reply but he's bent his head ever so slightly so that his ear is cocked closer to me, as he nods slowly while I talk about the ethics of having children, using that voice that James always calls contrived. It's a baseless remark and would surely crumble under scrutiny. But he doesn't prod too much because I suspect he likes his interlocutors to be as intelligent as he is, even if it's a spurious projection. We walk like that, so slowly that we start to bump shoulders, all the way to my job at the Greek restaurant and I stride around the whole night like I'm marching in a parade, pretending he's right there watching me.

'I'll tell you now, you're going to feel like the biggest asshole in the world if you keep this up,' Dan says in a voice note when I tell him about this thing with Nathaniel. 'You've been with James for six years. You're bored, so what? Grow up.'

This is Friday, and I know he can't find his passport so he's taking it out on me. But to be fair, he's always surprisingly loyal to James. Last year, when James was unemployed and depressed, he started doing creepy things like playing Edith Piaf in the bath and secretly reading my emails. When I told Dan, he was excessively kind, to the point where I thought he was being sarcastic, insisting that James needed my support and understanding. Even now he has left Ireland, I will still consult Dan on these matters and often, his opinion has the power to sway the course of my actions.

'Obviously, I was never going to do anything,' I start to reply. I end up recording the message and deleting it three times because I sound like I'm only saying this out of shame.

On Saturday, I wait in arrivals and see Dan before he sees me. He's walking with a travel cushion around his neck and looks a little irritated, as if he thinks I'm late. I start to laugh because I can see him mouth, for God's sake, and start to call me on his phone. I get right up next to him, laughing at his impatience, before he even realises it's me. There's a moment where he hesitates and I know that if I don't wrap my arms around his shoulders, we'll waste too much time feeling like we don't know each other so well anymore.

It takes us over an hour to get back because I can't remember where I parked the car. I've made a lasagne and we watch three episodes of *Buffy the Vampire Slayer* and then when the wine is gone, we go to the off licence for more. Then we come home to watch *Muriel's Wedding* but Dan falls asleep halfway through. When I get a message from Nathaniel, I mute the television.

Colleen! he writes. Friendly. A few of us are going to Lucky's tomorrow. You up for it?

I type my reply into the notes app on my phone before committing to typing anything: Nathaniel! Class, love Lucky's! My friend's home from New York and staying with me, so if he's up for it, we'll see you there! I delete the second exclamation mark, add a smiley then get rid of that too.

I watch the status under his name change from online to typing... for a few moments until I'm startled by Dan, who wakes himself up with an abruptly loud snore. I guide him upstairs and he sleeps in my bed, on James' side, on his side facing the wall.

'It's temp work, my new job.' Dan tells me the next morning, as I burn the scrambled eggs.

'I'm just sick of working sixty-hour weeks to support someone else's art,' he says. 'And what's wrong with wanting to work a normal job? What does it matter, once I can pay my rent, who cares?'

'Did you tell your dad?' I ask.

'Yeah, but I told him it's permanent and that there's opportunity for promotion. He's thrilled. Maybe I'll tell him I'm straight too, he'd love that.'

After I shower, I shout down to Dan that the bathroom's free but he doesn't reply. Back in my room, when I swing my bedroom door shut, he leaps out from behind it, causing me to shriek.

'Fuck you, Dan!' I say, grabbing my pillow and smacking him with it. 'Go for your shower, you stink.'

This shouldn't have been a surprise, not when he used to lie prone at the end of the stairs, his head turned at a funny angle, pretending he had slipped and died, when we lived together. I'd try to catch him out by hiding in his wardrobe but I wouldn't be able to withhold my stupid laughter for long enough. 'Colleen,' he'd say flatly, 'get out of my room.' As if nothing I did ever affected him.

'Will we go to Lucky's tonight?' I ask him, as we walk along Clontarf seafront with two 99s.

He pulls a face. 'I'll probably go there loads this week, Colleen.'

'The people from my class are going. You might like them.'

'Is Nathan going?' he asks.

'Nathaniel? Maybe.' My wrists are sticky, the chocolate sauce is after dribbling down my sleeve.

'Don't pretend you want to show me off. If you want to see him, we'll go,' he says.

I'm annoyed at him for addressing this with such direct calm. It makes me feel foolish, like my behaviour is inevitable and therefore unworthy of disappointment or reprimand.

At Lucky's, I spot Nathaniel sitting between two guys at a crowded table. There are no seats available so rather than loom over them, Dan and I stand across from the bar. I deliberately face away from them and do my best to focus only on what Dan is saying. His voice trails away for a moment and his eyes focus over my left shoulder. 'If James finds out, he will never forgive you, and I wouldn't blame him,' he says, with a thin smile, before walking away and nodding at Nathaniel, who has come to stand in his place.

We stay so long, it's like we're waiting everyone else out. I start to yawn in Nathaniel's face, I can't help it. Over the course of three hours, I begin to slowly regret this stupid little fantasy. The more he drinks, the more Nathaniel repeats himself. And he's rude to the bar staff. But it's too late now because he's walking along to the taxi with me and Dan and asking me have I any more wine at the house. God, the worst part is that he pulls out a grey tartan paddy cap for his head. I look up at Dan who is walking two steps ahead of us and wish he'd tell Nathaniel he can't come but he doesn't, he just walks along, swinging his shoulders and hips a little bit, as if he might start whistling.

Shortly after we get home, Dan says he's off to bed. I'm staring at him, hoping he'll meet my eyes for long enough to see I need to be rescued from this awful mistake. His eyes glide past mine and he leaves Nathaniel and I alone, on the couch. I stand up and make myself busy at the sink, washing my glass.

'No way, the shrine is a bit much, isn't it?' Nathaniel says.

I turn around and see him stand up to inspect the glowing Sacred Heart and the collection of religious items surrounding it. He pulls out his phone and starts to record a video.

'I have to put this on my Instagram stories, it's so fucked up,' he laughs.

'They're all Dan's,' I say, stupidly. I won't engage in any sort of analysis with him, I decide to treat him with an opaque kind courtesy, my answers short and leaden, like a heavy door slamming shut.

He stands over the items, tugging at his lip thoughtfully. I don't want to hear his insight; I don't want to hear any observation he has about what these items say about me or Dan or our culture. In this very moment, I'm disgusted with myself for caring about art and being impressed with someone like Nathaniel and for thinking I can reduce everyone I meet down to whatever it is that makes me pity them, as if people don't already know what their problem is. I don't want to see this man ever again and I wish I could tell him to leave now but the best I can manage is to tell him he can sleep on the couch. He's taken aback, lost for words, at last. I go to bed and I cry which is ridiculous but I call James and I tell him that I brought a friend home and that I feel terrible. I don't say anything about how much I pushed and orchestrated this because it would be too awful. I need him to know what happened but not why it happened. And he's so kind, he even laughs, and says he knows he can always trust me because I feel guilty about the silliest things.

I wake up after ten and creep down the stairs. There's nothing left on the couch except a crumpled-up blanket. I climb back upstairs and pause at Dan's room. I open the bedroom door, carefully. He's still asleep. I get a sudden urge to laugh and cover my mouth with my palm. How much longer can he sleep? I get on my hands and knees and slide my body under his bed. I lie on my stomach, my face against the carpet. If I can wait long enough, I might just be able to grab his ankle as he gets out of bed. Forget about desire, it gives me such pleasure, to imagine catching him out like that.

A Story

Stephen Sexton

written 10th October 2021

Fifteen miles trading third gear for second; the back roads' weird undulations and bends. For a few seconds I am disregarded by sheep, cattle for a few seconds, and soon I'm disregarded by nothing but the fields themselves, fenced by haphazard stonewalls and the steadier perimeters of hedgerows and the shaggy, patriarchal scots pine.

A left turn onto the main road. Civilisation becomes plastics factories and dormer towns, a few varieties of Presbyterian church. Both churches, vast and grey, have their own flourishes of austerity and, I'm told, their dwindling congregations. Big, hardwood double doors are riveted with Gothic studs, and the windows are set with modestly stained glass. Few, if any, scriptural episodes are played out by the sun. The Time is Short, says one church. Nothing, says the other. The road proceeds, and soon, growing into its bones like a teenager does, the village forms itself from clusters of houses in Courts, Parks, Crescents, Prospects.

If the main street were called Main Street, you'd say it was tautological: there's no mistaking it. In the childless playground, the apparatuses of climbing frame, swing set, slide, are painted Google-yellow, Google-green, Google-red. A strip of doomed commercial units next to the hardware store dabbles, every year or so, in the domestication of new cuisines. I miss, sometimes, its simplicity.

Beyond the newsagent-confectioner and the pub named for where the railway used to pass, is the mercy of the roundabout. Anywhere is three miles from somewhere, and here there are options. Off the second exit, Church Road is up the hill, so is the other graveyard and the certainly haunted, castellated home where indigent children and their mothers worked their fingers further into hardship. Countryside again. Not much farther. Through these fifteen miles, I groan and drum the wheel, and plead with Sylvia's Scenes.

STAGE & SET BUILDING THEATRE FILM TV

says her van, cautious and meek below the speed limit. If the oncoming lane wasn't the occasional true black of hearses—two or three—heading for the crematorium back towards the city, it was lorries from the quarry shuddering past. No passing. The lorries set off dragging their almighty burdens of stones at 5 in the morning to wholesalers and contractors in town, and don't quit until the quiz shows come on. They brim with gravel; they return nothing but themselves. In the queue outside the butcher's, people say it's the lorries tearing up the tarmac, coaxing new potholes out of it. It's hard to blame them: the lines get so long. People have to pass the time.

But Sylvia, what's out here? Where are you going?

I see a rustic setting of *West Side Story*, and I don't want to. Ulsterish Country and Western music, singers with voices smooth as slide whistles playing farmers' sons and farmers' daughters. Ninety minutes, plus encore, of land disputes and innuendo and square dances, stage winks at local jokes, the point of the thing dreadfully missed. Then again, I could be driving behind the Maltese Falcon itself, or an arsenal of broadswords, or a wardrobe of white coats and goggles and test tubes. Or the van might contain the wholesome, terrestrial ephemera that realises a space movie's first act: a clapboard wall, its window of barley—the image of home Johnny Saturn's forever wounded by. He cherishes it, and cherishes it more by pulling his space helmet on, and turning, facelessly, and leaving it. Who knows, Sylvia, if your cargo is bound for a new and distant planet, or simply for the dump.

My father's television rocks in the backseat. One corner I tucked in the footwell under the driver's seat. Just like that, first thing this morning: blank screen, no sound. All things pass. Backlights, inverters, capacitors. Thirteen years is going good enough, we agreed, especially since the television ran most of the day to keep up with hundreds of overs thrown at the Indian Premier League. Through the night, the television interpreted, into a dark living room, the sand traps and greens and links of pretty American courses;

adverts for irons and woods of extraordinary technical advancement: the greatest *turf interaction*, the finest bafflers.

My father is content with the lunchtime news blaring in brilliant colour from a smaller, dusty spare I carried, arms between its legs, like a sick dog, down the stairs from my old bedroom. Cuts to benefits, death rates, unseasonable warmth until the weekend. The bell dinged in the microwave.

And yes, warm enough, but overcast, the radio agrees. The rumour of rain even. The static prickle of ions in the air before a storm. The last mile and a half after the church. The quarry coming up on the right, the recycling centre thereafter on the left. And still, Sylvia, the two of us moving no faster than a reverend on his bicycle on a Sunday. It happens.

Some days, on the way to work, coming through the mountains sheer and severe and complicated, I find myself behind a convoy. Between the hazard-lighted rear-guard and the pioneering pickup trucks, there's a long, flat lorry with a cabin on its back. A golden-coloured wood: rooms, doors, windows, nice slating on a good, pitched roof. I decelerate, I turn off the radio.

For twenty minutes or so, the valley plunged below us, I walk around in my cabin. Everything is fire-lit. The floorboards creak in the kitchen. I fry eggs in a cast-iron skillet, the kettle boils on its trapeze above a stack of logs edged with flame. The walls are hung with the incredible tog of bear and beaver skins. I sweat in the animal skins. I grow my father's beard. I develop an enthusiasm for baseball. At the window, where moose trail in clouds of breath, snap and clash and strike and break like heavyweights about an unseen referee, I stare out into the pure snow of Colorado. I stare back at myself on the mountain road, descending.

At the quarry visitors must present themselves to the main office, announces a notice. And—farewell Sylvia's Scenes. The van accelerates over the hill, bears right, is gone.

A left turn, a speed bump. Meticulous lanes, grim, metallic industry. There are bins in which to deposit most of the mineral world: garden waste, wood and timber, scrap metal, fridges and freezers, large appliances, small appliances, TVs and monitors, portable batteries, car batteries, used engine oil, cooking oil, fluorescent tubes, paint, mixed glass bottles and jars, plastic bottles, mixed paper, food and drink cans, ink cartridges, textiles, books, gas bottles, plasterboard, rubble, carpet, mattresses and cardboard.

Just one car in the farthest corner. I coast, stop, activate the handbrake, kill the ignition. An older man, tall and lean and elegant in a navy body warmer and white shirt, carries an ironing board towards the scrap metal bin. There's sweat on his forehead, thin grey hair matted flat. Walking back towards a trailer, there is a woman about his age. Retirees, I'd say, if I had to. A good, long marriage. Too old for labour like this. Haven't they children to help with this kind of work? Haven't they nephews or nieces?

Their trailer is stacked with antique things of all kinds, most of which are indistinct except for age. She's walking across the pale concrete in her own time. She puts a hand on the wheel rim and lingers. There's suddenly the headiness of motor oil, or the sweet carbons of diesel. Plants of many fronds poke over the high walls. In moments, she draws a stout rug, rolled like a trapper's fur, and heads off across the yard towards textiles with it on her shoulder.

It doesn't take much to wrestle the television from the back seat. It's lost weight in the handful of miles between the console table it sat on for thirteen years riddled with scart cables, and the bin I carry it to. It's never easy to dump the thing so crudely, to blunt its corners on bounces. There are others, of course, redundant screens of all the recent generations—CRT, LCD, HD. Computer monitors too; whole machines, in fact. Any of them could have been mine. The Packard Bell monitor is lipped with rust, its speakers are slotted in like elephantine ears. The tower too. Buried in its psyche somewhere is someone's all-time top score in Solitaire or Hearts. Its browser preserves some of the garish archaeology of Geocities or Angelfire still: a webpage's visitor counter, a guestbook.

They've swapped places. Back at their trailer and stiff, puffing his cheeks, the man carries a pyramid of staircase spindles, or the detached legs of many tables—chipped white paint—towards its destiny. Returning to my car, I amble by. There's more, really, than the trailer should carry: paperbacks, bin bags of clothes, curtain rails, heavy radiators, ceramic lamps, mahogany panels of the sort to comprise a wardrobe or a dresser. There are doors, deck chairs, chunks of plaster, and picture frames with their photographs in them, brass knockers, black marble flecked with jade that was a fireplace. What kind of a home have they divested, the two of them. I shut the rear door, open the driver's side.

I start the engine, the air conditioning. The weather threatens to break, and it will, spectacularly one of these days. The woman seems to have vanished from the yard, but the man is at the trailer, which is practically empty now, except for hats. One on top of the other, he's stacking an extraordinary totem pole of hats. They are ladies' hats in all conditions of pastel: mauve and violet cloches, wide-brimmed Derbys, straw hats with outrageous red roses, a black velvet pillbox, a Gainsborough in teal, oversized mushrooms in peach frilled with organza, tulle, chiffon, taffeta. This teetering column he takes from the trailer not towards the bins, but rather the few awkward, shuffling steps to the back seat of his car, where they topple into the car, and where he falls after them, his brown brogues toeing the concrete.

I should go to him, I think. I should go to him.

And I would make the time to go to him were it not for the house being so cold tonight, so stripped of every fabric and cloth; any material that can hold warmth. The gale blows right through the hallway where, if there were doors, the force would take them off their hinges. The little kindling in the fire is ash for sure, and cold. I would go to him and take his hand, my friend among the beloved things of his life, and help him up, I would. Upstairs my wife is sleeping where it is warm.

Every Forest, Every Film

Marie-Helene Bertino
written 16th October 2021

When I first moved to New York, I took a job reviewing films for a poorly distributed, religiously read magazine and became known for being overly critical. Hating everything was my entire personality, another reviewer wrote on their blog. I lived in a one-room apartment where, for a design reason that remained unclear, the toilet was in the middle of the living room. When a guest had to use it I'd step onto the fire escape and listen to cars flash by. New York was thrilling and expensive and I spent most of every day feeling successful for staying alive.

One morning, my father left me a voice message I listened to in bed. He had sent me a package, had I received it? His usually placid voice was strained, the package must be important, I thought. *He wants to know. Received.* All day I checked on breaks from writing a review about a new film that was engineered around what I considered a clever use of the word 'ribald'. My father did not answer his phone all day and no package arrived. Towards the end of the afternoon I made spaghetti with pesto from a packet, keeping the windows open so I could hear a late delivery. Another feature of my apartment was that it was under the flight paths of both major airports. Planes flew overhead, filled with packages. Everything was a package.

The phone rang. I thought it might be my father but it was another reviewer calling to see if I'd take her job for that night. She said it was 'in the middle of nowhere or wherever the fuck'.

I mostly reviewed screeners and streaming television but she said this one had to be in person.

The Cab, it was called. Her tone implied that I should know what it was and be thankful for the opportunity.

'If this film is so great, why aren't you taking it?'

'Show,' she said. 'Not film.'

'Why aren't you taking it?'

'You really haven't heard anything about this, Milletti? Have you been out of the country?'

I told her I was as close as you could get to being out of the country while being fully in the country. I meant I had been in bed for the previous week and a half. She took it to mean I'd been having sex.

'Okay okay, girl, I see you.' She sounded impressed.

'That's not what I'm saying.'

She laughed as if I was being coy. 'I see you.'

She said the tickets would be left at the counter and I said that was fine but she'd already hung up. She was the kind of person who shamed someone while asking them for a favour. I admired her to the point of nausea. One more thing about her. Her name was Jude Law. Like the actor. That's not significant, it's just a detail. Rather, it's just as significant as anything else.

I had gone to bed because I'd seen a photo online of my ex from a wedding. He was wearing sunglasses and sitting next to a woman with an elegant neck. I thought about the picture when I soaped myself up in the shower and walked to the food store where I debated what kind of mushrooms would keep their integrity in the wok. Then I couldn't remember if he was wearing sunglasses or whether his hair was short so I looked at the photo again and again was overwhelmed by how little I cared so I crawled into bed and thought about the way his beard hair glimmered in the sun because even the sun favoured him. The photo pinned me the way stones pin a river.

The show was at a fancy multi-media museum in Elizabeth, New Jersey. I had to take a series of trains to get there and when I arrived I was sweating, gasping, and furious with myself that I had never strong-armed anyone into doing my job while acting offended and aggravated.

The multi-media museum was lit with purple lanterns that made the building seem like a giant reproachful insect. There was no movie signage, yet a line of people stood outside. My curiosity clicked on. At that time I was susceptible to the feeling of being in on a secret.

Inside the new-looking lobby was awash in carpet. Even the counter was carpeted. It reminded me of the roller-skating rink I grew up going to. The bumpers and walls and tables were sheathed in velvety plush so no one would get hurt if they fell. It made me sad to think about. In the winter of my sixth grade year I skated alone to Whitney Houston's 'So Emotional' thinking sad thoughts when my father, who'd arrived early to pick me up and had been watching from the side, yelled, 'Hurry it up, Milletti, I'm not getting any younger!'

There was a mix-up with my ticket. Jude Law hadn't spoken to the right person or they'd misplaced it. This seemed to require several clerks to join the original clerk to search and talk. I left them and went to the bathroom which was lit by more purple lanterns. A woman standing near the door handed me a paper towel and when I thanked her she said, 'I don't work here.' She wore a vest buttoned over a turtleneck and official-looking joggers.

A text from my father read: DID THE PACKAGE ARRIVE?

I texted back: AM AT WORK WILL CHECK WHEN I GET HOME.

He texted a series of emojis that signified being grateful, in love, and horrified.

Back at the counter more clerks had joined the search. One who seemed to command respect from the others said, 'This transaction was improperly handled from the start.'

The original clerk looked panicked. I battled my sympathy for workers for my desire to get in and sit down. Finally, the respected clerk asked if it would be okay if I sat near the back. I said that was fine, confused as to why it had taken so long to figure out when the answer had been a simple matter of seating.

I asked them how the reception to the film had been and they remained silent, blinking at me.

'This is the first night,' the original clerk said as the respected clerk said, 'This is the only night.'

I took my ticket to a curtained wall and a woman emerged and said she would lead me to my cab. It was the vested woman from the bathroom.

'I thought you said you don't work here.'

'I said I didn't work there,' she said, pointing toward the bathrooms.

She held back a section of curtain so I could pass into a country-dark vacuous space that evoked endlessness. I sensed large structures nearby and people milling about. The woman walked me to her cab which looked like an old subway car. I sat in the back. The lights went up inside. A couple up front gathered their things and left. My driver took her seat. She arranged her legs around the steering wheel and the train lurched forward. The feeling of real movement was uncanny. The giant window at the front of the cab and the small windows on either side were obscured by city muck. We were driving through a city I didn't recognise that looked like Paris *and* Vienna. Explosions fireworked over the horizon, some kind of power plant I strained but failed to see through the windows.

I felt I was in a rare and important work. 'This is very realistic!' I called up to her. She gestured to her ears and shook her head.

She turned onto a road that spiralled up a steep hill. The switchbacks were narrow but I remembered a story about bus drivers in the Andes Mountains, how they know their roads better than some people know family. I glimpsed sharp cliffs and reminded myself we were still inside the museum. Every so often she pulled off to the side so another cab could pass.

'When does the show start?' I worried I would miss whatever it was I was supposed to see. I said, 'It's as if this cab could be a theatre.' She nodded. Something hovered just outside of my perception. She accelerated towards a sharp curve at the end of the road. The speed felt real enough to make my pulse hop in both wrists. She sped up. I assumed we would need the speed to make the curve in the expert way years of experience had taught her. Instead, she barreled faster toward it until I was certain we could not make it around. I cried out.

She launched us off the ledge and we hovered above a valley of exquisite homes with lush gardens. The buoyancy of sudden elevation spread throughout my stomach and my ears popped as if we were actually climbing. I had never seen homes so beautiful as those we flew over. Owls and turquoise doors and wildflower gardens.

We flew towards a hulk of navy mountains outlined in the dying sun. As we got closer, they grew bigger and again my body reacted as if we were going to crash. I cried out, No! And, hey! The cabbie ignored me. I could see homes glimmering in the foothills and we slammed against the side.

At impact, the lights came up and the walls of our train were gone. I found myself in a room of seating arrangements being manned by their own cabbies, dressed similarly in vests and joggers. People gathered their things and left. Others arrived. I realised I was in the middle of a structure that had many beginnings. Depending on where and when you entered, each one was a different part of the show. But that wasn't all of it. When its people arrived, the train cars sprung up around them and flew away. I could see landscapes through the departing windshields that were different than the one I'd traveled through. I didn't see the same landscape twice. There were infinite shows. When the lights went up, those who'd reached their end would either leave or stay for another trip. The effect was disorienting. I no longer was certain we were in the museum. The sensation was like driving over the peak of a high hill. The sound was mountain birds in February, nesting.

Disoriented, I left the cab, found the curtained wall, and stumbled across the lobby. I tripped on a fold of the carpet and the contents of my purse spilled across the floor. I hadn't realised how many things I'd been keeping in there. Hair ties, coins, and lemon chews buried in pockets had launched away from me with violent purpose. A wincing woman stepped around the mess as if I had vomited. I was trying to gather everything when a large group of formally dressed men approached to ask how much certain items were. They held up my tampons, date book, the banana I carried in case someone was a diabetic, the book mark my ex gave me, my glasses case.

'They're not for sale.' I was angry and had a headache. Something about the show had dug a nail into me. I didn't want to interact anymore. I wanted to go home and get back into bed and after taking five trains that's what I did. No mail had come while I'd been gone. I texted my father that the entire day had been a disappointment, which felt appropriately dramatic.

In my uneasy dreams a package waited for me to arrive. I was on my way, but I was late.

I did not stay in bed when the sun rose like I had every other morning. I took the stairs to the sidewalk and walked into the street. Even New York City is quiet and carless at 7 am. I turned to the East as if it might yield a package. I turned to the West.

Returning inside, my phone was ringing. It was my father.

'Never mind,' he said. 'Your mother never took it to the post office. We're taking it later today.'

'What is it?' I said. 'What's in the package?'

'Your high school tennis trophy. We thought you'd want it. Now that you no longer have a husband.'

'My high school trophy? But that's not important! Why were you making it sound urgent?'

In the moment that passed I heard a plane climbing to cruising altitude.

'Sometimes,' my father said. 'I don't know how to talk to you.'

I wrote and filed a rare positive review that afternoon, but I was coming to the end of something. Lush soundscape. Triumphant second act. I was tired of rephrasing the same sentiments. Many people don't realise: every movie follows the same beats. I wasn't overly critical, I only wanted to return to the thought that endings could be different. This desire paired with my feeling that an important central force in the city that once loved me was now cruelly indifferent. When I thought of staying, I saw myself on a fire escape, trying to block the sound of a flushing toilet. I moved as south as one could while still being in the city limits, then into the forest. I can't be the first to say it: a forest is a verb. The measure of whether you're in one is whether you feel you are somewhere or just on the verge of somewhere. Something is always shifting out of my sight here. The gesture of being ever so slightly outside of reach.

When did you cut your hair?

REFLECTIONS ON A ONE NIGHT STAND...

Jon McGregor—

This was a terrible idea. This is not how writers actually write. I didn't even know what *The Stinging Fly* meant when they said they would be sending a *prompt*. When the five words arrived, I instinctively put them all in the first sentence, boxing myself into a corner from the outset. I wrote long-hand on A3 sheets of paper, and found that the structure of the story—a 750-word scene, a change of setting, repeat—was being shaped by the size of the paper. As were my coffee breaks. Each image or sentence kept suggesting the next, and I just kept going. It occurred to me at one point that in other artforms this is called improvisation. I remembered Bill Evans' liner notes for *Kind of Blue*, when he refers to the Japanese painting technique where the brush can't be lifted from the page without damaging the paper.

I ran out of steam around midnight, so I typed up the 2,000 words I had and went to bed. I slept badly while losing track of dialogue fragments, and got up at 5 am to spend the last two hours of my allotted time working between paper and laptop. I found a sort of ending by about 6.45 am, and wrote the last couple of paragraphs in that final quarter of an hour.

I loved working like this. What will become of me.

Rebecca Ivory—

I practise writing for an hour or two, four or five days a week, because even if the work isn't good, it helps me feel productive and maintain equilibrium. I care about my characters and the imaginary situations I subject them to, but sometimes I feel almost embarrassed by the extent to which I think about it because there isn't always an external demand for this. As much as I feel compelled to write, this exercise made me see how helpful it can be to be invited to write. Writing projects with an indefinite deadline tend to leave me feeling insecure and uncertain. In this situation, there was no time for self-doubt or excessive criticism. I just had to write about people and the decisions they were faced with and what this meant for them at a specific point in their lives. Between planning this on paper and typing the full story, it took me a little over ten hours. I realise afterwards that I have developed an unhelpful habit of trying to edit my stories before they have even been written, which is a completely immobilising approach. In having my own one night stand with a brand new story, I felt a genuine and renewed love and excitement for the practice, an experience which reminded me why I had started in the first place.

Stephen Sexton—

Although it was only a little frightening, I'm delighted to have been able to participate in this exercise, or challenge, or experiment, or experience, or quest. Whatever it is, not without a few considerations does one give oneself over to this kind of project. On one hand, twelve hours is no time at all to produce a piece of writing, guided only by a few key words. On the other hand, it's plenty of time: on a good day or night one might achieve something interesting or worthwhile in a third of the time, given a fair atmosphere and ergonomics, and a good synchronisation of humours. As I often remind myself, Chad Kroeger of Nickelback said in an interview that he wrote 'How You Remind Me' in fifteen minutes, and we have no reason not to believe him. Silver Side Up was the band's third album, though; they knew what they were doing. Instinct takes over.

I like stories, but I don't really know how to write them in prose; the poem is the more comfortable technology for me. I realised, as I followed a whim at 7.30 pm or so; at 9 pm and 10 pm, I was discovering and trying to discover how to make a story happen. What are its conventions, who is speaking, why are they speaking, how are they speaking? These considerations must come naturally, I imagine, to many dedicated writers of short fiction.

Most challenging, I think, was being confronted with my own lack of experience with creative prose fiction—I had little instinctive currency, and, being unpractised, no reflex to rely on. I was proceeding quite into the unknown in terms of content and form and genre. Rather than some sweet torrent of language, I tiptoed from paragraph to paragraph, gradually developing, like a pointillist, images or turns of phrase.

That the piece need not necessarily be 'finished' or 'polished' is something of a comfort, but nevertheless, one doesn't really want to expose the messy materials and devices of one's imagination, its imprecise or crude trajectories. However, that's part of the point of this exercise; to show work-in-progress or the work of a night. To put to one side questions of 'craft' or well-madeness is a refreshing prospect. I had fun, but it was not easy. For big parts of the many hours between 7 pm and 7 am, I fiddled with sentences and tried to kill the kind of manic syntax I found in front of me. I mostly tried to get to the end.

Marie-Helene Bertino—

I said yes to One Night Stands because I was interested to see what kind of froth and friction throwing what Tom Morris referred to as a 'bit of a mad ask' into the middle of my fall semester would create. Maybe An Important Thought would arrive alongside the prompt at 7 pm. It did not. So, I worked the story like a job, taking a recent wild dream and writing it as total fact. A storm gathered outside. I felt romantic. I rose early, made it as presentable as possible and turned it in, exhausted. I notice my sentences are unusually compound. Dead ends and creative detours that revision would usually snip have been allowed to remain. 'Buried' was the hardest word—I managed it with minutes to spare. Had I written the story a week before or a day later, it would have been completely different. The experience made me wonder how many other evenings have passed by unremarkably when I could have been producing a story. I'd like to try it again. Perhaps The Important Thought will arrive. Regardless, any evening spent writing—or any day, for that matter—is a good one.

Float

translated from the Catalan of the non-existent poet Alberto Cenas

Pollina, I see, has been writing—emphatically, asthmatically—about Cardona-Blanxart again.

He's made it into *El Riu Negre*. In Documenta, on Pau Claris Street, I pick up the April number.

Jobless now, I spend a long hour perusing the department stores, as if somewhere in Santa Eulalia I could shed the great freight of my liberty.

Poor Pollina: his obsession with Cardona-Blanxart so jejune, so unbecoming, his prose so disagreeably *grasping*.

Prose should hover and oscillate, should flit about and coax its subject, should be a hook upon a filament.

My father took me fishing once, on a secret swerve of the Francolí. I remember his rust-flecked tackle box, the lures that were cerise or robin's-egg, the serious glinting hooks.

He'd sit still for hours, leaning forward, a veritable *penseur*. He'd preside over the clicking reel, the rod that in his faraway hands flickered with such economy, the tangerine float flashing and bobbing on the river's listless bend.

I venture such details tentatively.

I fetch pickling salt for my mother's house, for the apartment that we share up on Granados Street. I fetch loin of Asturias salmon.

Poor Pollina. Why, only last month I was prevailed upon to furnish him enough for his bread and board and sundries—a not inconsiderable tranche of my allowance. It is an advance, one fears, destined to be long in the remittance.

In the Muñoz Garden, beneath the avocado trees, I finish his dank missive.

No, my father's float, I can practically see it now, was a jittering emerald sphere.

I fold the ink-scented journal.

Sun haze. Old men about the lily pond. The hovering Fenollosa twins: Ariadne with her half-smile, glittering Anaïs. So pellucid-skinned, so buoyant in their posture that they seem to merely flirt with density.

Prose should be a hook, a spooling filament.

Poor Pollina.

One must sit still for hours.

Billy Ramsell

At Casa Almirall

translated from the Catalan of the non-existent poet Alberto Cenas

I could have lingered, gentlemen,
till the first drafts of the morning,
till the dawn with all its tangerine, its amber,
caresses this old stain-glass partition.

I could have tarried in this candle-lit back section
amid these cockles,
these slivers of octopus.

I could have given hour after hour
to the appraisal of vermouths,
of variable vintages,
while skeins of cigarillo smoke
hover about the ceiling fan.

Ah I could have lingered here!

But I, as a minor poet
of the Catalan neo-renaissance,
am summoned to my duty now.

Oh Gonzalez, oh Pollina,
I must arise and leave you both.

I must forsake this raised and delicate
soufflé of conversation,
must sway down Joaquin Costa Street;
through the standing heat,
the weed lividity, sour canyons of the Raval.

I'll go north. I'll tend the grapes of metaphor,
work my allotment of the language.

How I've tilled those ingrate terraces:
the pared back squares of lavender,
the topsoil perfumed and unyielding.

Slowly. Slowly.

My verses stretch and hesitate,
scale their rickety trellises.

My fruit comes rust-red, grudging.

My muse is the muse of chalk,
of ingratitude and lavender.

Billy Ramsell

True Story

Anonymous

[TEXT MESSAGES: 05/09/2019]

I had sex with [him] yesterday right (too much detail) and then this morning he just had a go at me saying he "can tell I'm Not enjoying it" and then just walked off
10:04

This entitlement to sex thing is so wearing and then if I do make the effort, admittedly I don't really want to, he then has a go at me 12 hours later anyway
10:04

It's not good is it
13:06

It's starting to make me feel a bit sick
13:06

And like he hasn't spoken to me since but now he's sent me a meme on Instagram
13:10

What is this
13:10

And then he has started this new thing where he starts saying "you dont love me you're going to break up with me", which feels pretty difficult to answer when then the next minute he'll be like "you don't like sex" and then "what's for dinner"
13:59

—

An evening in late January. A woman is walking down a residential road, shopping slung in a tote bag on her shoulder. It's freezing out but she is walking slowly in circles, having to switch the mobile phone from one hand to the other because her fingers are whitening with cold.

I think it's time to pack a bag, her mum is saying.

The woman stays in the cold a few moments longer to talk to her mum, saying over and over that he's not violent, not like that, and how would she get the cat out in a rush?

She lets herself in through the front door. She pauses, listening for whether her boyfriend is at home, not knowing whether he will be in a good mood or a bad one, whether he'll surprise her with a gift or whether he will ignore her or shout at her. Nothing: he's out. She puts the shopping in the kitchen, then she goes to the bedroom, reaches into the wardrobe for the backpack that she normally uses for weekend breaks. Oslo, Amsterdam, Paris. In the bottom of the bag is a triangular plastic device for splitting headphones, which her and her boyfriend use to watch one of their TV series on a train or a plane. She finds her passport first and packs it along with a jumper, some jeans, some medication. A phone charger. The end of a packet of chicken biscuits for the cat.

She zips up the bag and places it under the bed, pulling down the edges of the blanket to cover it. Then she returns to the kitchen, unpacks the shopping and starts to make dinner for him.

—

My therapist told me that I hadn't once mentioned my ex-partner's name until after I'd left the relationship. I had become too anxious to name him in a confidential therapy session.

There's an unhelpful focus on why women don't leave abusive relationships. It is a cliché to say that you have to be in the situation to understand why you cannot see beyond its boundaries, but a lack of boundaries is how abusive relationships function: passivity and dissociation become the primary ways in which you cope. There are no bad things, only things that happen to you. Some days, these things are almost bearable; some days they are worse. Some days I would be cleaning the shit left in a toilet by my partner who refused to speak to me but fully expected me to tidy up after him; some nights I would run a shower after sex to cover up the sound of my being sick.

Abuse tends to take place gradually, over a long time; but once a boundary line has been crossed, it will always be crossed again. Timings, tenses and limits become blurred. The first person narrative voice will become the second or the third as, increasingly, it will feel like everything that's happening is happening to someone else. Your living situation can deteriorate at the speed at which you can be sitting in front of the television watching *Top Boy* and, the next minute, without any preceding argument other than your cat chewing on a pot plant, you're being dragged across the lounge by your collar.

Did I understand why I had made him angry? Did I understand that he wouldn't switch the television back on until I agreed that I could see why he had to behave the way he did sometimes? I nodded and, as the television restarted, asked myself if what just happened really did happen. Was it really so bad, I asked myself? If it wasn't that bad, why had nobody ever done this to me before? We watched the end of the episode as if we'd paused it to make a cup of tea. Crouched on the edge of the Ikea sofa that we'd bought together, as he told me to stop fucking fidgeting because it's hard to concentrate on the TV when I won't fucking sit still, it would be difficult for me to think at all. Not for the first time would I feel dumb, inarticulate, incapable.

Forty-five minutes' later, after I'd fed the cat, he initiated sex with me. I let him as it was easier that way, although he shouted at me afterwards all the same. He could tell I wasn't enjoying it, he said, and that spoiled it for him. Why don't you let me know when you're coming home from work so I can just have a wank instead, he snapped, and I wondered then if I'd imagined the sudden snatch of my collar as I'd stumbled back across the living room.

—

[TEXT MESSAGE: 29/05/2019]

He was so shitty on the weekend, on Friday he like grabbed [our cat] by the scruff of his neck and lifted him up to "discipline him" and I had a go as like you can do that when they're kittens but not big chonky cats, and then on Saturday he had a go st me as we hadn't had sex for like 3 days

10:57

—

On average, 1 in 3 women in England and Wales, and 1 in 4 in Ireland, will experience domestic abuse during their lifetime. Having experienced gaslighting first hand, it is remarkable to me that any victim has both the evidence and the confidence needed to convict an abuser. I can re-read all of the messages that I wrote at the time—date-stamped, double-ticked—but they can still seem like someone else's story.

I am just feeling like I have gone a bit mad. [My partner] and I had another big argument yesterday about him hating [where we lived]/ wanting to buy somewhere together [...] and this morning it came up again as more of a conversation, and I keep saying I just feel really unsure because it's been such an unstable year and I have found his behaviour quite upsetting at times and it hasn't made me feel secure in the relationship, and he keeps saying that we haven't really had any big arguments for a long time and this is my insecurity and I can't give him any specifics about things he has said or done, and I feel like my memory is now quite confused.

09:35

One day, he asked if I had turned my phone screen-down when a message came through because I was talking about him to my friends and how I was planning to break up with him. After that, I turned off my notifications and never left it in a room with him alone.

A friend later told me that she never asked about the relationship or used my partner's name in messages to me because she was worried that he was reading them. I myself often omitted his name, and what was explicitly happening, in messages: either because I was trying to blank it out, or because I was scared he'd read them, or because I was so buried under a sense of what was normal for us.

When we talk about abuse, it's often supposed that women know exactly what's going on but don't want to admit it to themselves. For me, the aggression and capitulation in my relationship was so normalised that I had been made to feel responsible for my situation. Talking to or about women as if they are wilfully ignoring a problem places further culpability on the victim. Rarely do we ask what the situation looked and felt like to them. Instead of asking, why didn't you leave, what would we learn if we asked: why did you stay?

At the start of our relationship, he installed the Find My Friends app on my phone, and would often check where I was. At the time, I thought he was looking out for me. Control and care can feel interchangeable.

He had written me a letter on Valentine's Day, three days before that evening when he grabbed me by the collar. He wrote that he loved me. He told me that I had been the kindest person in his life and he never wanted us to be apart.

He told me that he felt lucky to have found and kept me in his life. He told me that he loved how I was around his friends and family. He told me that he loved my body and that making me enjoy sex was his favourite thing to do.

—

Earlier in February 2020, a friend advised me to call a charity to plan a safe exit. He wouldn't do anything to harm me, I kept saying, even though two weeks beforehand I'd been swallowing back sick during sex that I didn't want but had let happen to me because I was dreading the repercussions if I said no. I felt worse afterwards, when he told me that I didn't make enough of an effort in bed and sometimes it felt like he was raping me.

It wasn't the first time he'd said that I had made him feel like a rapist. Eighteen months before that night, he had used the word 'rape' on a romantic weekend away.

We were meant to be on a holiday abroad but he'd cancelled it the week of the trip; this was something he did often, whether a few days before we were meant to travel or at the airport itself. I wasn't allowed to be upset by these sudden decisions, as it made him feel bad; I wasn't allowed to apply for insurance claims, as that made him feel bad too. Over the years, I had to lie to his friends and family about having gone on various trips abroad, or they'd make him feel bad too. It's your job to make me happy, he'd say.

So on a wet weekend on the English coast, we did the galleries, the bars, the city's two cathedrals. I took a photo of a Tracy Emin installation and he asked if I was going to post that shitty little picture on Instagram. At dinner, as our tacos arrived, he pointed out that the waitress was really hot. You could suck on those titties, he said; it was a phrase he used a lot about women, whether referring to my friends or his, strangers, colleagues, or my sister. But then he said a lot of things, and after telling me that evening that having sex with me felt like rape, he did what he would also regularly do, which was to not speak to me at all.

—

[TEXT MESSAGES: 23/01/2019]
He was in such a bad mood yesterday so I cooked dinner and cleaned the whole flat and helped make dinner for tonight (some of his mates are coming over) but then this morning he is all like, i hate it here, everything sucks
10:06

And on the way out of the door (apologies I am ranting now) he was like well
we can't buy a house together anyway because we never have sex. I am so ill why
would we have sex when I am coughing away
10:08

He was actually nice and fun and sweet in the past week but it feels really
cyclical and every few weeks he blows up like this
10:11

—

If you are told to do something over and over again, it becomes easier to do what you're told rather than entering into a circular argument about it.

I joined a gym because he told me I wasn't exercising enough. I don't want a fat girlfriend, he'd say. None of my exes were fat.

I stopped taking anti-depressants because he told me he couldn't be in a relationship with someone who was taking them.

He told me that I couldn't sleep on my back because my breathing was too loud. He would wake me up in the night, saying I had woken him up. Once, when I was ill with a temperature and a cough, I slept on the sofa because he needed his sleep.

—

A landmark judgement on rape, in the context of domestic abuse and coercive control, was issued at the Royal Courts of Justice in 2019. The original hearing had leant heavily on the threat of physical violence as a necessary element in the definition of rape; the appellant had not physically attempted to stop her partner, or shouted or screamed or tried to get away, and so it was deemed that she could not have been raped.

However, through the subsequent appeal, the defence sought to differentiate between submitting to sex and consenting to it: just because you don't physically stop someone from having sex with you doesn't necessarily mean that you are actively consenting to it. In order to consent to having sex, an individual must have both the freedom and capacity to make that choice: context is everything. In a coercive relationship, an individual may feel that they have no agency; 'no' is not an option. In this particular case, the appellant 'had let the father have sex with her as it was easier than to keep saying no'.

—

[TEXT MESSAGE: 30/07/2019]
he keeps calling me irrational? Like all the time? Which I am finding really
disorientating
23:27

—

Steam is rising off the rooftop pool and the spa is busy with couples and mother-and-daughter duos. It's the Christmas holidays and a Salvation Army brass band is playing in the street below. One couple is floating through the jacuzzi jets, the woman's arms around the man's neck and his arms under her thighs, carrying her. He's talking about his ex-girlfriend: she's not sure how they got onto the topic but he is in a good mood, so she lets him go on.

A few months after we broke up, he is saying, she sent me an email saying that I'd done all this stuff that was abusive. Can you imagine? She was crazy.

The woman doesn't say anything but she nods. His face is close to hers and he is laughing and making wacky expressions to underline just how mad his ex was.

She's heard about this ex-girlfriend before: how creative she was, how fit she was, how she used to love having sex. Although he's discussed his ex multiple times over the past three and a half years, he has never mentioned any accusations of abuse. It feels like a very specific piece of information to have withheld.

He'll probably give the woman an expensive Christmas present after this; he likes buying her gifts and referencing them for months after. I'm always buying you nice stuff, he says. Gifts mean that he loves her; sometimes they mean that he's sorry. Never mind that he was screaming at her only the day before when the car windscreen wipers stopped working. But the next time that he shouts at her after today, she will think: I wonder if he shouted at his ex like this?

Abusive, he said; crazy, he said. It's like seeing the corner of a card hidden up a magician's sleeve: a gift of its own.

—

[TEXT MESSAGE: 22/02/2019]
Yesterday he also said the only reason he'd had mental health problems was because we don't have sex enough? Which seems pretty unfair and unrealistic?
But also it makes me feel like I am failing the relationship
17:36

[VOICE NOTE: 25/01/2020]

'He then got hysterically upset and started saying I think you're about to break up with me and I think I would kill myself if you broke up with me and he was crying for hours and it was horrible.'

—

His unstable mental health is my fault. He has anxiety because I don't have sex with him enough. If he did cheat on me, which he could do, this would be my fault. I'm the reason his sleep is so bad. It's my fault that he doesn't like where he lives because I should be putting my savings into buying a home with him. It's my fault if he's put on weight because I should be cooking healthier meals for him. I'm always having a period, he says, this is my fault too. He's not going to have this conversation with me if I'm crying. All I do is moan all of the time. It's not his fault that I'm unambitious or I'm not working hard enough. I'll never get a book published, the way I'm going. I'm not as good in bed as his ex-girlfriends. I used to be so skinny, that was so hot. I was different when he met me. I probably was, I think.

Can you please try not to raise your voice at me or be so confrontational, I'll try. Of course I'm going to be confrontational if I am disagreeing with you, he says. You're so uncommunicative, he says, even when I have been trying to explain that I'm feeling anxious because he's been shouting at me since he got home. That night, he will be such a sore loser at a pub quiz that the host will actually call him aside to tell him off. Even though this does nothing to stop the ensuing argument that he will have with me on the way home, it is a relief to see someone else noticing something off about his behaviour.

—

[VOICE NOTE: 25/01/2020]

'There was a lot of, um, like, er, difficult language like, er, he was like "you're accusing me of saying this, you've said this and you're collecting evidence by writing things down, you're treating this like a competition". All really, er, quite bizarre? Um. And I'm really trying to be very, um, communicative and I've said, like, the way I probably haven't been super communicative before is because he's always been quite confrontational? And like, having a conversation is often like having a row?'

—

It started by him saying he would not be able to travel on planes or trains without me. Then he couldn't go to certain social events without me. I cancelled my evening and weekend plans. He couldn't cope if I went away for the night. And then he said that he would kill himself if I left him.

It's something that abusers say, I was told by various people. But I became genuinely terrified that he might kill himself, or try to, whether or not the relationship continued. I pleaded with my partner to go to the GP or speak to a therapist. I messaged his family and friends. One night when he was out drinking, I contacted a mental health charity for advice, using their anonymised webchat service on a private browser window before the lines closed at midnight.

His threats of suicide created an ultimatum-led environment in which I could not say no, or reason, or ask for anything. Perhaps he truly was, and still is, ill. However, as a friend of mine said, it didn't matter: whatever his mental state, he chose to exhibit controlling and aggressive behaviours solely towards me. His friends and family thought he was fine; in reaching out to them for support, I realised that the man I lived with was not the same one who they saw for dinners, birthday drinks or football outings. I appeared unbalanced. He'd probably been telling them that I was crazy, like his ex. And in turn, that made me doubt myself even more.

He has not killed himself. LinkedIn, the one platform where I initially forgot to block him, has since notified me that he has a promotion. Mutual friends have shared posts of him dancing, drinking, smiling. He never needed me to cope with living his life; he just used me. In the months before we broke up, when I explained to my family that I could not leave him, my mother described me as his slave.

—

[TEXT MESSAGES: 15/05/2018]

He doesn't really want to talk to me

22:25

Yes we're in the flat, I don't really know what to do. He says he can't have an adult conversation with me if I'm crying

22:31

I feel so pathetic

22:31

—

I was told repeatedly by him that the argument we'd had the week before did not happen, that certain things were not said or done, that I had imagined things, that no he was not shouting, that no he was not ignoring me, and that I was being wholly irrational.

I was being irrational when he took his hands off the car steering wheel on the motorway in the middle of an argument about pooling our savings, and when I pleaded with him to put them back, he held his hands up even higher to prove the point that I was wrong about it being unsafe.

Sometimes I said such stupid things. I was being irrational when he dragged the cat out from under a chair by one of its paws, saying that it needed to be punished for being noisy in the night. I was irrational when the hob was left on, the front door left open, the tap left on, two bottles of vitamin tablets left out on the floor for the cat to eat. I didn't know if he did all of those things on purpose but I was told that it was my responsibility to check. Have you checked? he started asking me when we left the house.

I became hyper alert to all noise, light and movement. My jumpiness became a running joke in the office. I started to throw up in the mornings, earlier and earlier. I developed idiopathic allergic reactions, my skin blooming in red welts my whole body over, and, in a sad symmetry of stress, the cat started pulling out its own fur. My short-term memory began to fray. The effect of gaslighting was so overwhelming that, more than any apology, all I wanted was for someone to confirm what was happening to me.

[DIARY RECORDS: April 2019]

Wednesday	Really hard to leave home, did not trust I had locked up. Left work early.
Friday	Stressed out.
Saturday	Very worried I had forgotten something.
Tuesday	Worrying had sent wrong email to wrong person.
Friday	Worried about locking up and leaving the house.
Saturday	Worried about cat.
Sunday	Mum saying that [he] hadn't treated me well at Christmas.
Tuesday	Very anxious about going into work. Didn't sleep well.
Wednesday	[He was] shouting about [a] watch.

—

[TEXT MESSAGE: 14/09/2018]

I'm finding it so upsetting that one day things seem fine then the next it will spiral into silence and I get anxious to bring it up as he is so argumentative. I think I need to say something tonight though as I can't cope going into work every day

14:12

—

I developed OCD to such an insidious degree that my partner encouraged me to start taking photos when I left the house to prove to myself that I had not done something wrong. Taking photos made the doubt worse. Some days, I could not turn the corner at the end of the road because I couldn't believe in the photograph that I'd taken only a few minutes earlier. Leaving the house took up to thirty minutes by the time that I'd recorded everything: taps, windows, the oven, the hob, the candles on the mantelpiece that had not been lit for months because I no longer trusted myself to blow them out.

Did I shut the door? I would ask my partner when we left for work; I don't know if you did, he'd say, but you have a real problem there. The level of doubt permeated every decision and action I made, so that I felt as if I was continually shorting my circuit.

I initially found a therapist to seek help for my OCD. Within a few sessions, she told me that my compulsive checking behaviours were symptomatic of a lack of safety at home.

—

There are currently 512 deleted photos on my phone. Two thirds of them are photos of doors, windows, the hob, plug sockets, candles, bottles with caps screwed on.

—

Gaps exist in the archive of women's experiences because to put your name to certain histories, however carefully or anonymously, could injure you. When the story you're telling pertains to an ex-partner who has bullied you, then the fear that something bad will come from its telling feels real and rational. It is not inconceivable that they would seek to control what you say and how and to whom, because that was the dynamic of your relationship. The doubt created by gaslighting left me questioning my own words. Even now, I wonder how could I stand up in a court of law, when I couldn't trust myself to lock the front door. After all, I'd been told for years that I was imagining everything.

I did not experience the same levels of violence and sexual assault that some women do, but domestic abuse and coercion can take, and often evolve through, subtler forms. My unremitting thought—'but was it bad *enough*?'—is not a question that women should ask themselves, or that anyone should ask of them. It does, however, answer why women typically only attempt to leave a relationship at the point at which it becomes physically violent. Violence shouldn't be the only signifier of abuse: it often won't be a sign until it is too late.

—

While the relationship was deteriorating, we still went to weddings, family occasions and birthday drinks together. I went to work, regardless of whether I had been shouted at or raped or told I was ruining his life or told I was the only good thing in his life. People would say that I looked tired. Some of my friends knew that things at home were bad. After the break-up, they expressed sadness that they hadn't known the full of extent of what had been happening. They thought that what they'd known was bad enough; I had thought that what I was experiencing wasn't. He will properly beat you up next, if that's what you're waiting for, one friend had said.

The week before my partner grabbed me, my therapist wrote DOMESTIC VIOLENCE on her whiteboard. I later told her that I was amazed by her prescience. She explained that she had thought that some forms of violence had already been happening for a long time.

—

[CHARITY WEB CHAT: 12/03/21: 21:21:]

I am generally doing much better and feeling less anxious; I think what I have realised more recently is that I am feeling quite angry about what happened to me and just want to try and understand why, even though I know there aren't really answers

—

A questionnaire on womensaid.org aims to help women identify problematic behaviour in potentially abusive relationships. Questions include whether your partner checks up on you or follows you; if they criticise, belittle or insult you; if they have hurt or threatened to hurt you; if they have forced you to have sex or participate in sexual activities; if they have prevented you from taking medication; if they blame their mental health for their behaviour.

—

[TEXT MESSAGE: 06/10/2016]

I am feeling quite stressed as i am wondering whether to go back on the antidepresssanrs after having had a break from them, and I dont know whether I do want to go back on them or not really, but mentioned it to [him] and he has got difficult again about them saying he isn't sure he can be in a relationship with someone who has to rely on medication [...] He says he still wants to be with me but it just seems such a contrast to how he has been

10:50

—

[TEXT MESSAGE: 07/03/2019]

[He] is so up and down; he has generally been nicer and bought me flowers and even cooked, but he still hasn't acknowledged any of it or said sorry, and [it] still feels like [his] mood could flip

12:26

—

There came a time when the labels that my therapist gave me would feel empowering, because they offered clear demarcations of what is and what is not normal or legal, what I should and should not expect to experience in a relationship.

Initially, words like 'abuse', 'coercion' and 'rape' made me feel like a mug. I read repeatedly that women with low self-worth are susceptible to abusive relationships: another implication that this was all my fault, confirming everything that my partner had been telling me for years.

My therapist explained that I had been raped, pointing out that that was the word my partner himself used to describe having sex with me. With my diary, we pinpointed at least two occasions, eighteen months apart, when he had said this to me. Even within the first three months of our relationship, almost two years before I can remember him bringing the specific word into the bedroom, he had pressured me into having sex in spite of recent abdominal surgery that had left me in severe pain and for which I was on extended sick leave.

My therapist later told me that she'd tried to raise the issue of sexual assault several times, but I had been made to feel so complicit in what was being done to me that I could not see it. Feeling guilty doesn't mean you've done anything wrong, my therapist told me; making you feel guilty is how he'd coerced you throughout your relationship.

—

According to research carried out by Australia's Domestic Violence Prevention Centre, a woman will, on average, endure 37 incidents of abuse or coercion before attempting to leave an abusive relationship. Typically, physical aggression and violence occur—and often will only start to occur—around the time at which the women leaves, or attempts to leave.

—

[VOICE NOTE: 20/02/2020]

'He didn't hurt me but, um, it was just, I don't know. In that, I had that moment of thinking like, oh God—um, is this, um, it this how it all starts?'

—

[TEXT MESSAGE: 23/02/2020]

My mum is bringing a bolt to put on the door

00:05

Now, writing about my relationship feels like the only way to regain any control over a series of events in which I had no agency. Writing is bearing witness and at that time, I would have wished that anyone—*anyone*—could have witnessed the humiliations that were happening to me on a daily basis to confirm that no, I was not imagining them or asking for them. I felt like I was, in a sense, my own witness because I disassociated from what was physically happening to me. If you are made to feel scared in your own home when someone is simultaneously telling you that they love you and they couldn't live without you, then it is only possible to exist outside of yourself.

Towards the end, I started leaving friends voice notes. At a time when it became impossible to call friends from home in case he overheard my conversations, it became a way of communicating urgently, and with love. Now I can listen back to a message in which I sound distressed or disassociated by turn, describing how I had been shouted at, or threatened, or called irrational, or coerced into sex to avoid a row. While I did not tell everyone I knew every single thing that was happening to me, friends were worried enough to give me the emotional and practical support that I needed to leave.

For all of the reinforcement that my friends and family gave me, it was only after I left the relationship—when my ex's initial pleas and love letters dissolved into open anger and bizarre material demands—that I started to see it for what it was. My therapist encouraged me to write a list of incidents, or patterns of repeated incidents, to curb any recurring doubts or guilt; my list stands at 45, and counting.

If we, as a society, want to get better at both preventing abuse and supporting survivors, then we need to talk about the subject more openly. Rape should be on the curriculum. Domestic violence should be on the curriculum. Emotional and psychological abuse and coercion should be on the curriculum. Mental health is not an excuse. You are not irrational if someone says or does something that harms you. Know your legal rights. There are always two sides to every story, but there are also facts, dates, times. Record them, if this is happening to you. Tell your friends through text messages at the time when the events unfold, and delete your sent items if you have to: they can, and will, keep copies for you. Call your family from the street when it is not safe for you to speak to them in your own home, so that they know to pick up when things get worse, because they will get worse. Talk to a counsellor, if you can, because they will confidentially log everything that you've said has happened each week. Speak to a charity on an encrypted webchat and save the reference number for when you need it. Pack a bag, get spare keys cut. Keep receipts and download your bank statements, especially if you have a joint account. And write. Write everything down, every word you can think of: I wrote the words on my phone and my email drafts and the theatre tickets that I used as bookmarks and in the small notebook that I kept in my spare backpack in my locked drawer at work, because all of this is true.

Air

down

through
noiseless
breezes

fall
gently
from

the trees
again

down

turning
in grace-

ful contact

slowly

turning

in a
warmer
upthrust

up too
    & sideways
light

then down

landing
in place again
without a I

went back
to / work I
dust rising

silver
& green
outside

went back
to
I

lifting

turning pages
shifting
boxes

3342

to get to
this
piece of—

persistent
piece of—
whose

birthday
is it anyway
(dark)

& what
is it to/
what

is it
time
to

442231

(now)

throw
away
next?—

this
persistent
piece of—

darkness—

darkness
on yr
desk

a splash zone
round a
crater

that sound of—
hold still—
failure is it? ...

whisper-whisper
go the
terminally

envious
in a sudden
run of

pent
malice.

.

that's it—decades—doctorates—
centuries
of the

woven babble
of the species—
let

the honey-
combing
begin

cada
mañana hago
mi

cama then
squirt a
splash of

Death's Door
estate bottled
darkly rich

its
black blood
hit bottom

as gates—windows—
bang in the
storm

(berry, fig, leather)
giving the
wind

its energy back—
threatening delighting
advising cajoling &—

scribble
scribble

shiver of richness—
fine-tasting
poison—

almost ripping yr roof off.

dusk. disturbance
among the
blackbirds. night.

.

& so dear god the 19th century
melts into
the 20th

the 20th into the 21st
rain-damaged
useless

but keeping shape
while you slept
then radiates &

radiates & *radiates* &
believing (grieving)
(feeling) radiates

& (erasing, retrieving)
radiates &
(watching

attending) (wondering
absorbing) (re-
imagining &

un-remembering)
stressed links in a
chain of stories

(*turn that page now!*)
(&) sorrowing
too

(flickering antennae
a dot stopped
on a

lower leaf) &— through
a thin break
in the mist—

radiates still.
what then is your
castle made of?

blank.

& your garden?

fallen apple-shell
where a bird
had fed.

salut!

.

sinking back
into the
bed

the soft
the sweet

thinking she said for
long for happy
for

murmuring o
bent over
you

o pouring love
for so for
soft

for what *is*
this stuff for
you o

love o
love for
you

tang art
tang

pungent-dazzle-
leaf-touch-
thrill!

.

that rumble
of rhetoric
(click-clack)
that whisper

of the actual—that.
quick march! heel. turn.
erase. click. where?
click. there. air?

spare it.
not another
word.

.

oyé!
Carmen!—José!—
down through the little village—
late & dark—

down into the
twisting streets
nobody thinking—

threading—really to
sleep here this
time of year

luxuriate
instead in
the

slight cool
of night
whose

chance-breath-breezes
play silk against
the skin—

& overhead—
stars!—a
pulsing avalanche ...

.

of course
there'll always be
a reason to be

happy somehow.
somehow. if
the ground of

being is
threaded
through

to the name
of the thing
as part of

the eman-
ation of
the thing

anterior to
the naming of it
so that

emanation
& name re-awaken
enwound

each thing
thus woven as
thing-perceived ...

dot in a
vast network
each itself

a
mere
dot

in a single arm
of a single
galaxy

in a sea of
billions
among

which
worlds in which
life in which

this violent overactive
species moving
in to kill …

put yr scrap
in the panicle
anyway

a dead leaf
dancing in
the breeze

descending
quietly
down

then up a
little then
down again

this
way
that

through
time

time-in-light
& space-
in-time

to
here.

Maurice Scully

Luigi Lucheni
Michael Phoenix

I first heard about Elisabeth, the Empress of Austria and Queen of Hungary, from a woman on the terrace of a Budapest café. The café was on a hill on the Buda side of the Danube, and I sat facing the direction it climbed, looking towards the woman across the table from me, with my back to the rest of the city.

She was very tall, the woman said. Thin, though not as thin as they say, and afraid of narrow staircases. She refused to sit for portraits once she turned thirty-one, or it could have been thirty-two, and started to angle her face behind a fan around the same time. The easy interpretation is that she wasn't trying to preserve her image but an image of herself. As she got older she obsessed about her weight. At one point, they say, she weighed herself two or three times a day. She smoked, I've heard heavily, at a time when celebrated women rarely smoked. She was also an amateur; an acrobat and a horse rider, and when she turned fifty she took up one of the sharp arts of self-defence. Her first child, a daughter, died of typhoid before she turned three. Her son, when he was thirty, killed himself and his seventeen year-old lover in a bloody murder-suicide pact. The coward. The Empress and Queen suffered from depression, disliked her husband, and kept herself at a certain distance from their two other children. Many people, though not everyone, and I don't think even herself, thought her exceptionally beautiful, but what does that matter?

In early September 1898, when she was sixty, Elisabeth travelled to Geneva. She made the journey unannounced, using a false name, and took just one lady-in-waiting with her. Not long into the visit, she was assassinated by the French-Italian anarchist Louis 'Luigi' Lucheni.

The woman slid a packet of strong mints from her pocket, took a cold blue pastille out of the packet and placed it in her mouth. The sun was white over us and shone without much heat. From behind me I could hear the weight of a tram pulling up the hill and slowing. The woman looked past me as the tram arrived at its stop and I took the chance to look at her more closely. There was a brown mole on the corner of skin between her left eye and eyebrow. Her eyes themselves were lavender blue.

The waiter passed and the woman turned her gaze from the tram and put out her hand to stop him. She ordered an expresso, with an *x*, and a glass of water. I asked him for a glass of beer and we watched the well-dressed Hungarians and the ex-pats off the tram as they walked past us and away into the rich hills of Budapest.

Lucheni was born in Paris in April 1873, so 'Louis', the woman told me, without a father he was going to know. His mother gave him over to one of the city's foundling hospitals the day after he was born. From there, after he turned one, they sent him to Italy, Parma, and its system of orphanages and foster families, so 'Luigi', the name he went by. He served three years in the Austro-Hungarian Army, though no one can tell you exactly when anymore. What's clear is that sometime after he left the military he emigrated to Switzerland, first to its Italian corner, then across the German-speaking zone and finally into the Francophone region, where he fell in with anarchists from the Jura mountains—Jurassiens.

The waiter brought the woman her coffee and her water, but he didn't bring my beer.

Lucheni stabbed Elisabeth with a sharpened file on the Quai du Mont Blanc, along the west bank of Lac Leman, which gets called Lake Geneva; there's a statue of her there now, in the spot where the act happened. He would have been twenty-four, or maybe twenty-five. He was caught by passersby as he fled the scene; in fact they were workers, and they held him until the police arrived and arrested him. I don't know if he was beaten, but, when I consider it, my gut tells me he wasn't.

The woman paused then, as if deciding whether to continue. She held herself steadily, slightly relaxed into her chair, and looked at me directly. Maybe she was waiting for me to speak, to say something about Lucheni, or about something else, but I couldn't think of anything to say. I looked back at her and wondered how she and I had ended up at the café, how we'd begun talking about Elisabeth, Lucheni. I wondered how she knew so much about them. In the end she cut away the last of her coffee in one quick turn of her cup, then went on again.

Lucheni was tried as a common murderer, as opposed to a political criminal, and was forbidden from making any declaration at his trial, political or otherwise. After that the verdict wasn't in doubt. Capital punishment had been abolished in Geneva in 1848, so when he was found guilty he was sentenced to life in the new prison built within the Évêché Castle in Lausanne. There, after almost ten years doing what, I can't say, he set about writing his memoirs, which were later seized and destroyed by his prison guard. On the 16th of October 1910, he was found hanging in his cell. Most people I know, or who have bothered to write about it, say that he killed himself. It seems likely. He was thirty-seven years old.

To me, the cruelest part of his story, of what happened to him, not what he did, might be what became of whatever he wrote in prison. Why did the guard destroy it, if that's in fact what he did? Was it out of some kind of fervour? Love for Elisabeth? Or fear? In a way, clearly, it was an act of murder too.

I've been wondering about them, about Elisabeth, Lucheni, since I came back to Geneva. This is where I am now. I'm standing on the Quai du Mont Blanc, near the statue of Elisabeth, in the present like four years before.

I have just arrived then. It's the middle of July and the city is incredibly hot. The sky only seems to move between three shades: thick blue, pearl and pink. The most important points in the city are its geographies of water; the two rivers and the lake. Hawks and gulls turn above them. I've never heard of Elisabeth or Lucheni.

In the early evening, before the heat of the day has become the heat of the night, I walk out the tight streets and dense shadows of the city's old hydraulic quarter, away from the conflux angle of the Arve and Rhône rivers. On the street where I've rented a room, there's a building constructed the year I was born that has never been used. It has a faux-marble front, a steel security door, windows doubled up with wood. I'm alone on the street when I pass it, its door crossed with melting glue from old security posters. Beyond it, I turn along the bridge and the iron and concrete L-pass over the mouth of the Rhône. I walk across the east-west tramlines and make towards the lake. Where I reach the quay people sit in groups, drinking; others pass on their way to swim. There's a place I've come to prefer just beyond the main swimming spot, by a park maybe half a kilometre further along the quay, in the direction of the Botanical Gardens, where the path curves north around the roots of a sycamore tree and stretches out of sight.

I take the sycamore as my guide and make a line towards it, moving east to west following the quay until I reach the park. Not long into it, following the low wall that skirts the lake, I find the deepcut set of half-hidden steps that lead down to the shore. From there it's only a short way to pick across the lake-side and reach the water's edge. When I get there I dip my hand through the cool surface. As the city sits in the large of the map, I'm west of things here. East, on the other side of the lake, beyond the lower, drier mountains, the Mont Blanc climbs into snow.

One night, in the present, I overhear a rumour concerning Lucheni. I'm with a group of people I don't know well. We're standing in the front yard of a bar behind the station. The yard is open on the side that faces the footpath, the street lamps and the road. Everyone else is drinking glasses of amber beer. I drift away from the conversation; the foreign language. In the autumns since that first summer in the city, I've realised that Geneva is a place of parks; across the road from the yard is another. And for a moment I see—I imagine—that a doe appears between its trees. And when I do I think of you. Then I hear the name Lucheni.

Luigi Lucheni. Or Louis. She told me there's something of his in the library.

The voice is attached to a group just beside ours. It's the voice of a quiet man. He's very tall and I think of Elisabeth. Which library?

The one attached to the University. I was told they had burnt all his manuscripts, but apparently no, apparently they did not.

I don't know what the man means by 'they'. In Budapest the woman only mentioned 'a guard'. 'They' implies more. Or does it? The possibility of more, or a disembodied thing, a personified historical movement. I didn't realise that when she said 'destroyed' the woman had meant 'burnt'. But maybe she hadn't.

I don't know where the woman is now. I don't think of her often. She and I have moved in different directions, along with all the others that were meant to. I think about Elisabeth, Lucheni and you.

There are many ways to say the same thing.

It's autumn, three years before I hear about Lucheni, and we're in Geneva together. We have returned from travelling, thin and hungry, and have set about eating like pigs. Beyond the many meals our days have become typical. Brown, yellow and red leaves are strewn about them. Geneva is a place we're starting to grow into. We've walked the bend by the sycamore tree and are crossing the Botanical Gardens. You're out in front of me, suddenly deciding to run, and your cheeks go clean and red as you do. Beyond you, beyond the Botanical Gardens and over the border to France, and although there'll be weeks yet before it reaches us in the city, the highest lines of the Jura Mountains are already under snow. Large birds, dark blue, file from the lake in morse-code, in the direction of the mountains. These birds, I think, are rooks. As they cross the sky above the gardens you turn towards a black tree, with cobwebbing branches sphered by light orange fruits, and slow down as you reach it. When you do I catch you up, and before I've read the sign at its base you tell me it's a kaki tree, from China; that a kaki's fruit is a precise thing, dissimilar, that you eat as soon as you get home with a glass of cold water. We take two fruits fallen on the ground, either that day or another, because we come back to the gardens again, then turn for the path that loops back by the sycamore tree to the lake. And when we get back to our apartment we set these things out, open the back curtains and window for rooks and late sun, pour out two glasses of freezing cold water, slice the fruit and make love in the light that cuts across the living room.

I decide to search out Lucheni's manuscript. I come to the decision late one night, walking along the Quai du Mont Blanc towards the statue of Elisabeth. The path there is quiet but for distant trams and buses and the movement of birds on the lake that can't be made out in the night. When I cross other people, when they cross me, we take our hands from our pockets and hide them close to our sides. As I come towards the statue I pass a woman. I sense that I might have known her, that she might have looked at me, but I keep walking without looking back at her. Only when I reach the statue do I stop. And there are other distances there, within its bronze folds: the past hiding away from the world along the quay.

I've passed the statue many times before. It's the work of a Scottish sculptor. He chose to draw Elisabeth's waist impossibly thin, leaving her unreal and alien, royal. But I've not come back for her. A friend has written from the

Jura region. Elisabeth looks away from the quay, he says, in the direction Lucheni walked off in. Walked, because I hear he didn't run. I find the line of Elisabeth's gaze, then turn in a hemisphere to follow it away into the city, in the direction of the station. As I do my line of vision crosses a very different kind of sculpture: a large, hollowed-out man sits on a thin bench, leaning forward, his head leant down towards his empty chest, his elbows on his knees.

I wake the next morning with a dull pain in my side and a sense of fear and urgency. I search the website of the university library for Lucheni's manuscript and find the record quickly.

HIST-GEN; LIBRE ACCESS – REZ
VIII 4 LUCH
BFCA 134 286
1070945300

I pull over my heavy coat and move off into the context of these letters and numbers.

It's winter, almost a year and a half before the here and now. You've left the city and have no plans to come back. I cross the lake from the Pâquis District in the direction of the centre, and start uphill towards the new apartment I've taken near the hospital. It's not late, but already dark. On the road the traffic goes by as though the cars forced their way through ice, and the city and us among it are broken into strips by their headlights.

I turn into the park that borders the old university building. The gamblers playing chess at the boards by the entrance stand huddled in tight squares. In an hour the park will close, the players will have to leave, and the pieces they've been moving will stand static in the cold. My hands go into my coat pockets, by my keys and my phone. Leaving the Pâquis District I bumped into a friend of yours, a man studying physics and philosophy and other things I know nothing about. As I walk through the park I feel the conversation between this man and myself tugging at me, then falling away, moving somewhere parallel. Maybe I move it there. I've not eaten, and the hunger sits in me like a dull weight. The trees that guide the path through the park are lit with installations of luminous plastic birds. Somewhere in the south of Spain the rooks of the autumn gone are feasting. Through the exit of the park

I come to the French Embassy. Yellow candles are lit along the pavement at its entrance, close to going out.

When I get to the apartment I fry a thin cut of fish, keep the skins on the potatoes, add salt. I would like to be with anyone. I turn the radio on, the Swiss and European news, brittle music, then turn the radio off again, take on my winter coat, and go back out into the night.

Much later on I call you, but you don't pick up. The next morning I wake to a missed call, but for some reason I don't return it. I leave the apartment early. I don't eat before I do. And on the way to the place I have to go that day, through the thin grey snow that has started to fall, I say to myself: at the end of the month you'll be going from this city and you'll never have to come back.

The library is in the basement of the university building by the park. Its first stone was set in 1868. Its rooms are tall and filled with a compressed, subterranean cold. I speak to the man at the reception desk.

Yes, he says, Lucheni. But you cannot access that.

I don't know what to make of his explanation for this. Near the reception is a desktop computer. The man leaves and I sit down and search the library catalogue—LUCHENI. There are four pages of results. Of them, I can only access a French newspaper clipping: La Presse, 11 September 1898 – L'assassinat de l'Imperatrice d'Autriche, Sissi. I look through the other results. There are four or five books in French. Each has a similar title, more or less close to Le Régicide Lucheni. They appear to have been written by criminal anthropologists, mainly during Lucheni's lifetime. Apart from the books, most of the results come from academic articles with titles along the lines of: 'An Investigative Psychological Analysis of a Lone-Actor Terrorist'; 'The International Anti-Anarchist Conference of 1898 and the Origins of Interpol'; and 'Nineteenth-century Anarchist Terrorism: How comparable to the terrorism of Al-Qaeda?' They appear in journals called The Journal of Threat Assessment and Management and Terrorism and Political Violence. On the final page of the search results I find a link to a journal based in Lausanne, an article by a Swiss historian, C. Cantini. I take a piece of loose paper from a box beside the computer screen and copy down the article's title. Then I make back up the stairs and out of the library building, into the bright, freezing day.

*

Cantini named Lucheni as 'Luccheni' in his article. It was the only place I found the extra *c*. Reading through what he wrote, I discovered a great deal more about the man's life, along with details of the assassination of Elisabeth; the investigation carried out by the authorities in Geneva after the killing; the identities of other anarchists—in particular from Italy—installed in Geneva at the time, as well as in Lausanne, and on the outskirts of both cities; the relations, or suspected relations, between these anarchists and Lucheni/Luccheni; quotes from his trial; the reactions of the bourgeoise and proletarian press throughout the affair; even the views of Italian migrant-workers unionised in Switzerland. After all of this, I found the opinion of Cantini himself. The historian ends the article by stating the following: 'Ultimately, the explanation of the act is to be found in the inevitable collision between two worlds, two diametrically opposed worlds.'

It's spring, the present, the middle of the day. I'm walking on the Quai du Mont Blanc. The sky is blue above the lake, moved by the gulls. I pass Elisabeth's statue and think of Cantini's article. It's been several months since I read it, but the copy I printed is still in my bag. On the edge of the park near the Botanical Gardens, not far from the sycamore tree, I walk to the wall that skirts the lake and take the pages out. I re-read the article standing there, leaning on the stone of the wall in the fresh sunlight. When I reach the end I realise I've made a mistake. The last line, which I remembered as I translated it, is not as I thought it was. The explanation of the act, says Cantini, is to be found in the inevitable collision between two *morals*, two diametrically opposed worlds. I can only translate the first clause directly from French. *Morals* is what the word he uses seems to mean, but I don't understand.

Once, you asked me, To what point do you think we live our lives symbolically? And I don't know. I still don't know. Though perhaps it was me who asked the question; perhaps I asked you.

Respice Finem

Pungent waft of raw meat
From the market stalls
Smells like pussy on the
Middle finger of my
Left hand
I am living alone
In Mexico
And have only a loose grip on
Well, the language, to start.
(These are the days of my life)
((These are the days of my life))

Lucy Sweeney Byrne

The Johnny

Liz MacBride

The blow of coming home was softened by not having anyone left in the Pale to actually miss. All the people I'd associated with in Dublin had been Christopher's friends, and since I was no longer his girlfriend they'd been relieved of the duty of tolerating me. Lucky them. Christopher called sporadically on the landline, as my mobile rarely got reception in the house, to tell me how beautiful New York was in the autumn. He called it *fall* on the phone, and he called New York *the city*.

When the calls dwindled and then stopped altogether, I flirted with the idea of killing myself. That'd teach them. I hadn't clearly defined the lesson, or who *them* was supposed to be, but I figured it would teach someone somewhere something, and wouldn't that be nice? A Domestos and rodenticide cocktail perhaps, in one of the Waterford Crystal flutes my mother kept locked away for special occasions. I pictured the glass smashing as I collapsed to the floor, my mother's dismayed face as she collected up the broken little shards. Collateral damage. Unavoidable. The steeple of the Protestant church was also briefly entertained; the possibility of being impaled by the wrought-iron fencing adding a sexy, dramatic flair to the whole thing. Maybe the fall would bisect me neatly at the hips, and I could have a coffin that split apart like a magician's box, so people could pay their respects to whichever half of me they had preferred.

Ultimately, I decided to just stay alive. I was afraid of what Mary Frances might think if she knew I was ready to throw myself into the Suir over something as trivial as being grotesque and fundamentally unlovable. I wanted her to keep believing I was a person who had the mental fortitude required to exist every day; the kind of woman who didn't need a man, or anyone at all. Mary Frances Mooney lived down the road and would probably always live down the road. I admired her consistency. In primary school she'd constantly had a yoghurt stain somewhere on her uniform, a detail I found compelling mostly because in the eight years we'd spent there, I'd never once caught a glimpse of her ever even eating a yoghurt.

When Mary Frances heard about my return, she dutifully turned up at my front door like a frumpy little homing pigeon. She liked accompanying me on my miserable walks along the back roads, inquiring about my former life: did I know anyone with the copper coil; did Brazilian men on rickshaws really sell drugs up and down Grafton Street in broad daylight; was it true Trinity made you line up in order of who got the best grades when you went to collect your degree? Mary Frances was so soft, almost gelatinous, which struck me as deeply unfair. Certain softer parts of me had long since calcified, yet there was Mary Frances, still the same as she'd ever been, her innocence some kind of miracle.

A few weeks after I got home, Mary Frances invited me to spend Halloween night in the Hole with her cousin Aoife and Aoife's boyfriend Lockie. The Hole was an area of woodland on the outskirts of the village where people went to drink, and to participate in the kind of other activities you'd expect to occur in a place called the Hole. The final frontier of girlhood, it had always been a rite of passage to have your breasts fondled clumsily for the first time by some clammy, acne-riddled teenage boy in the privacy of its many little nooks and crannies. Mary Frances told me to meet them by Bridie's corner shop and we'd walk over together. I arrived to find Lockie shivering outside in a Superdry jacket, collar turned up, his breath puffing out in front of him in the cold, depressing, unpolluted October air.

'Mary Frances is in with Aoif cashing up,' he said. 'Shouldn't be a mo.'

'Cool,' I said. I'd lost my virginity to Lockie when we were seventeen, though it didn't seem like a great idea to mention this now.

'D'you want some cider?' He held out a big plastic bottle of Devils Bit.

As we walked through the village I reminisced with Aoife about the camogie team and all the girls we'd gone to school with who were now embroiled in various multilevel marketing schemes. She'd just landed some job with either the homeless or the old, or the homeless and old—I hadn't quite caught the specifics. When she spoke about it her face lit up and she looked nearly beautiful.

'What were you doing in Dublin?' she asked.

'Theatre, kind of. Stage managing and that.'

'Anything we might've heard of?'

The last thing I'd worked on had been a piece for a student theatre festival, this shoddily done speculative dystopian satire of reality television set in a mother and baby home. *Keeping Up With the Magdalenians* had received vitriolic backlash on a large, almost national scale; an admittedly impressive feat for an amateur production.

'Ah,' I said. 'Nothing really. Bits and pieces, like.'

Kids dressed in black bin liners and cheap rubber masks occasionally bombed past us, towing along huge Aldi bags-for-life full of sweets. Some of them held sparklers in their hands, and I watched the embers pirouette as they ran. Aoife complained about the rental situation in the city to me and Mary Frances while Lockie struggled to roll a spliff beside her. Everything smelled faintly of firecrackers and the sweet, familiar sting of fresh manure.

'I haven't had Devil's Bit in ages,' I said to Lockie. 'Very retro.' The affected, drawling accent I'd taken on in college made the words sound callous and patronising, and as I heard my own voice I felt my face flood with a warm shame.

'Hah,' he said. 'Sure, this is it.'

What I liked most about Lockie was how he didn't seem to think anything he had to say was particularly worth being said or heard. I imagined Christopher calling the taste of the cheap cider *Proustian* while some eager past version of myself nodded in agreement.

Just before the road started to curve around towards Duncan's Bridge, Mary Frances stopped ahead and turned to face us with her arms crossed.

'It's freezing,' she said. 'I don't remember it being this far a walk.'

Lockie took this brief pause as an opportunity to finish rolling the spliff he'd started, deftly darting his tongue along the edge as we watched, enthralled. He tucked it behind his ear, then took out his phone, turning on the flashlight and holding it under his face.

'Wanna hear a scary story?' he grinned. 'Get the blood flowing?'

'Oh, give over,' said Aoife. 'You and your stories.'

'What's the story?'

'Yous ever heard of the johnny?'

'What's scary about a johnny?'

'*The* johnny,' he said, resting against the small stone wall that separated the main road from the farmland and motioning for us to gather round. 'So, yous know about Paddy Shaughnessy?'

'That old nonce who owned the farm?' asked Aoife. 'With all the dogs?'

'Scéal is Shocko got some young one up the duff years ago.'

'No way,' said Mary Frances. 'Who?'

'Dunno,' he shrugged. 'The family kept it real hush. She went over on the boat.'

He paused now to pluck the joint from behind his ear, lighting it and passing it to Mary Frances as he exhaled. It was bitterly cold and getting darker now, the sky overhead like a new bruise.

'So your man did himself in,' he continued, 'in that gammy shed at the end of the family land. And apparently now he haunts this johnny in the grass over there.'

He nodded to the overgrown field stretching out beyond the bridge, all purple-grey in the moonlight.

'How's it haunted?' said a wide-eyed Mary Frances, passing me the joint.

Lockie shrugged again, standing to stretch his legs. 'It's on the way,' he said. 'Could go for a look.'

'Go see a condom in a field?' I laughed. 'No thanks.'

'Wow,' said Aoife. 'Big city girl too good for us culchies and our haunted johnnies?'

By now the spliff had burnt out, and I mimed flicking an imaginary lighter. Lockie tossed me his Bic, smirking.

'Maybe she's *scared*.'

'Ooh, are you scared, Kath?'

'No.'

'Scared of a little johnny?'

'A little johnny in a little field?'

'No! Fine. Jesus. Let's go.'

Lockie swung his legs over the bridge, leaping down to the field below. Vibrating with Dutch courage, he stormed ahead of us as we followed suit, swiping down long grass and nettles with his feet.

The Shaughnessy land was wild and overgrown from years of neglect. Like a cemetery for useless things, household waste was scattered everywhere—

soiled nappies, a cracked flat-screen television, a decaying carburettor. I could see the trees surrounding the Hole from where we stood, little flickers of light and movement suggesting others had started to gather there for the night. It was late afternoon in New York and I hoped Christopher had eaten lunch, and that he'd remembered to drink enough water during the day.

'So,' said Mary Frances. 'Is this it?'

The corrugated metal roof of the shed was rusted and half-caved in, and vines snaked along the crumbling stone walls. 'It's around here somewhere,' Lockie muttered, scanning the ground. 'Aha. Here.'

We peered at the space illuminated by his phone's flashlight to see a wilted condom lying in the grass. I crouched to get a better look. It appeared totally ordinary.

'Oh,' I said. 'Great. Really scary.'

'I don't get it,' said Aoife. 'What's haunted about it?'

'It never leaves this bit of grass.'

'That doesn't sound so bad,' said Mary Frances.

'Does it *do* anything though? Kill people? Curse 'em? Ten years of bad sex?'

Lockie stuck his hand down the front of his Canterburys, absentmindedly scratching his balls. The waistband of his boxers poked over the top, his toned muscles visible through the fabric. I looked at the condom then back at him. He withdrew his hand.

'Nah,' he said. 'Ghosts can be boring, like. It's not all mad stuff.'

'So you're saying all it does is just never leaves this bit of grass?'

'Yeah.'

'That's really shit.'

Aoife and Mary Frances wandered over to the shed, inspecting the surrounding undergrowth. Laughter rose from the direction of the Hole. It sounded like a good time.

'Is that the whole story, Lock?' asked Mary Frances. 'Surely there's more?'

'Not really. Your classic old pervert, young brazzer tale.'

'Jesus,' I said, still fixated on the unnerving darkness where the johnny had been illuminated.

'Can't believe your parents didn't tell you this story,' Lockie said.

'Yeah, right,' Aoife laughed. 'Parents wouldn't tell their little girls stories like that.'

'Why not? What'd they tell yous?'

'Nothing.'

Noticing a branch nearby, I bent down to pick it up while the others kept talking.

'I didn't even know what a vagina was until you told us that time,' said Mary Frances. 'Remember, Lock? Katie Gaffney's eighth birthday party, you came in pointing at us all.'

'Oh my God,' Aoife said. 'I remember that. Poor Mrs Gaffney.'

'*Yous have fuh-chinas,*' Mary Frances laughed.

'Himself thinking he's Einstein.'

'Christ,' Lockie said. 'Leave it out.'

'Here, lads,' I shouted. 'Watch this!'

As they turned, I used the branch to launch the condom across the field. We watched it soar through the air in silence, landing in a ditch nearby. Nobody moved.

'You've fucked it now, Kath!' said Lockie.

'What? Now it's left this bit of grass?'

'Maybe we should look for it?' said Mary Frances.

'It's in a massive ditch, like,' Aoife said. 'We're hardly crawling through a ditch for an old johnny. Let's just head on.'

Aoife adjusted her jacket and started to move towards the woods, but Mary Frances hung back, dithering.

'Well, maybe we could figure out where it landed…'

'What are you gonna do?' I said. 'Calculate its fucking parabola?'

Aoife and Lockie snickered. The people in the Hole had started letting off fireworks, Catherine wheels and horsetail shells whizzing out from behind the trees. The sky flashed red then green then blue.

'Come on,' I said. 'Let's go over. Don't be such a dry shite for once in your life.'

Mary Frances looked at me like a kicked puppy.

'Relax,' said Lockie. 'I was only messing. It's just a story.'

'Then how was there an actual johnny here?'

'Young ones are always riding out here,' he said. 'Or do I need to teach you the facts of life and all, Mary Frances?'

'Yeah, grand,' she sighed. 'Whatever. Let's just go.'

We marched through the Hole's serpentine trails in single file before coming to a clearing in the woods. Dozens of locals our age loitered around smoking and smashing glass bottles with other glass bottles because there was nothing else to do. Lockie and Aoife seemed to know everyone, smiling wide and hugging them when we arrived. They were so happy to see us.

Lockie rolled more shit joints, and the rain subsided. We drank a lot and talked a lot, mingling with the other Hole-dwellers, people with familiar faces but names I'd forgotten who drifted around offering us the dregs of their drinks—straight vodka, Bacardi bottles with lipstick-stained rims, warm half-drunk cans of Strongbow and Carling and Tesco lager. We met an 18-year-old called Podge who offered us ketamine. I thought he might try to kiss me, but he didn't, and I didn't try to kiss him either. Instead, Mary Frances gravitated towards him over the course of the night, as if she had something to prove.

'Kath,' Aoife said after a while. 'She's off her tits.'

She nodded over to Mary Frances, giggling on Podge's lap across from us. His eyes were closed and his head rested on her shoulder. Most of the talk had lost its coherency at this stage, Hole-dwellers already skulking through the trees in the direction of the village. There was nothing left to drink and nothing left to smoke. Empty bottles lay strewn around us, and I watched as Lockie puffed uselessly at the roach pinched between his thumb and forefinger.

'Is she gonna pull him?' Aoife hissed. 'Do we definitely know he's of age?'

'Ah, yeah,' said Lockie. 'That's Damo's little brother.'

'You're messing,' I laughed. 'She fancied the arse off Damo in school.'

'Shh,' Aoife hissed again, 'or they'll hear yous.'

Mary Frances swayed in Podge's arms, whispering things in his ear that seemed to embarrass him. I couldn't remember the last time I'd seen her so drunk. There was something uncanny about it, like seeing your father cry. Podge's hand moved down her waist while she caressed his neck.

'You okay?' said Lockie, his breath hot and rancid in my ear.

'All good.'

'What do we make of the lovebirds?'

'I wish them luck,' I said. 'I really do.'

'Shit,' Aoife said, scrambling to her feet. 'They'll need it now.'

Across the way, the lovebirds had broken apart. Mary Frances knelt over a pool of vomit on the ground while Podge looked on in disgust. We rushed over, shoving him aside. Aoife pulled her long hair off her face and I patted her gently on the back.

'That's it, babe,' Aoife said. 'Get it out, get it all out.'

Mary Frances retched and coughed while we held her. The wet gags sounded extraterrestrial. She shuddered and hunched over, throwing up again. It had the colour and viscosity of menstrual blood and smelled like rotting grapes.

'Sorry, sorry,' she said. 'I'm sorry.'

We sat with Mary Frances through the dry heaves while Lockie and the remaining boys talked animatedly beside us. She curled into Aoife's arms like a baby, her jeans ripped at the knees and her forehead slick with sweat.

'Think it's time to go home,' said Aoife. 'What do we think?'

'I can take her.'

'You sure?' She eyed Lockie and the others.

'Yeah. You stay. We'll walk home, right Mary Frances?'

'Kath,' Mary Frances slurred, pulling me towards her. 'You'd make a good mam.'

'What?'

'Sorry,' she mumbled. 'I'm so sorry.'

It took us almost twice as long to walk back to the village. Mary Frances kept tripping over her own feet, shuffling along the icy roads like a beetle. We'd had a lot of nights like this in school, only with our roles reversed. I watched her now, staggering beside me, looking like she'd been dragged through a hedge backwards. I wanted to protect her from the whole world. When we reached her driveway I smoothed her hair down and gave her a hug.

'How're you now?' I asked. 'Better?'

'Mm-hm.'

'Good. And you've your keys there, yeah?'

'Yeah,' she said, holding them up proudly.

'Okay, now open the door there, alright?'

She fumbled awkwardly at the lock, her fingers white in the porch light. I covered her hand with mine and helped her turn the key. The door clicked open and she stepped inside.

'Listen,' I said. 'Before I go. I'm sorry for earlier, you know, saying you're dry. You know I'm glad to still have you as a friend here.'

She clicked on the inside light and stood there, bathed in soft orange. Mascara ran down her eyes, small splotches of dried vomit dotted around her mouth.

'Why'd you come back, Kath?'

'What?' I'd never known Mary Frances to say things that were on her mind.

'Why'd you come back?'

'Surely there's enough rumours going around about that already.'

'Dunno,' she said. 'I don't listen to gossip.'

'Maybe you should, then. Most of it's probably true.'

'Which parts?'

'Depends what you've heard, I guess.'

She didn't answer. Her face pale, she pointed behind me. 'What the fuck?' she said. 'Do you see that?'

I turned and looked into the gloom. 'What am I supposed to be seeing?'

Mary Frances switched on her phone's flashlight. A crumpled condom lay on the ground under the birch tree in her garden, a short distance from where we were standing.

'The johnny,' she croaked.

'It's *a* johnny.'

'*The* johnny. Holy shit, it's real.'

'You're pissed,' I said. 'Come on, you can't be serious.'

'Oh my God. It's actually real. We're being haunted.'

I took the phone from her trembling hand and walked closer to the condom, lying flaccid and wrinkled on the dew-flecked grass. It had the same ribbed sides and reservoir tip as the one from the Shaughnessys' field.

'It's not even the same as the other one,' I said. 'Now help me find a stick or something.'

Mary Frances appeared behind me and wordlessly handed me a branch.

'What are you gonna do?' she whispered.

Using the stick to pick up the condom, I carried it to the end of Mary Frances' driveway before flinging it over the gate and across the road.

'Did you expect me to perform an exorcism or something?' I said. 'Come on.'

I frog-marched her down the hall and she flopped onto her bed. Her room was full of odd knick-knacks: antique lampshades, dusty picture frames, porcelain dolls with lobotomy eyes. I sat down beside her on the single mattress.

'Will you stay with me?' she mumbled into her pillow. 'There's pyjamas in the bottom drawer of the bureau.'

'Okay,' I said. 'Can I borrow your toothbrush?'

"Course.'

In the moonlight everything looked blue. I changed, eyeing my stomach in the wardrobe mirror. What had been in there? What could it have been? Nothing. Gas maybe. Nothing worse than a bad tummy ache. Nothing alive, nothing real. I walked to the window to draw the curtains.

And outside in the garden something flickered in the bushes.

There, in amongst the chrysanthemums, was a johnny.

The johnny. Draped across a floret, quivering lightly in the breeze.

I drew the curtains, my pulse thumping in my ears. It was horror filmesque, a cliché. Without brushing my teeth, I returned to the bed. I'd had a lot to drink, that was all. It was nearly dawn, and I'd had a lot to drink, and my mind was playing tricks on me.

Mary Frances was already asleep. Her duvet cover was a map of the world and I counted constellations of blu-tacked glow-in-the-dark stars on her ceiling until my head stopped spinning and I slept there beside her, in fitful disjointed spurts, my dreams full of dead old men in dilapidated sheds swinging from the rafters on umbilical cords. Condoms rained from the sky. Christopher appeared and told me he was God. I had unprotected sex with my retired camogie coach Ger on a bed of nails, screaming *yes Ger, give it to me Ger!* Subsequently I gave birth to a Ger-faced baby, gurgling up from between my legs with a joint in his mouth, offering it to me as he began to suckle at my breasts.

I woke up and listened to her rhythmic breathing. I wasn't sure what time it was, but the dark sky outside the window had softened to an exhaust-fume grey, and I could hear the sound of cars embarking on their morning commutes. I assumed Christopher was in bed by now, that he was going to sleep holding somebody else, a thin New Yorker with a podcast who dressed head to toe in thrifted designer clothing and brewed her own kombucha, a gorgeous girl he could introduce to his parents, take hiking in the Adirondacks, marry, have kids with, die beside after a long and wonderful life.

Christopher used to say sometimes that I scared him. He used to say it was so cool that nothing ever seemed to bother me; he said I was so funny, that I had the kind of ass girls only had in rap videos. He liked the way he sounded when I listened to him speak. I made him sound so smart. Oh, whatever. He gave me things too. I liked the texture of his life, the way he softened all my edges. Now what? Who needed me to hold them close at the end of a hard day?

Mary Frances stirred beside me in the bed, her delicate snores syncopating with my shallow breaths. I turned to her and watched her sleep. The johnny was probably still outside, it was probably still waiting for me in the bushes. Maybe I'd go out there right now, in only my knickers and Mary Frances' oversized T-shirt, drop to my knees and cradle it in my arms. Who's to say it wouldn't follow me home, keep popping up at inopportune moments: in the postbox, the U-bend under the kitchen sink? Would I cradle it each time? Or bury it in a makeshift grave and hope it never came back? Things had been very boring for a long time—at least a curse would break up the days a little bit, give me something to do.

I realised now that Mary Frances was awake and looking at me through half-open, unfocused eyes.

'Did you have any dreams?' she asked quietly.

'No. I don't remember. Did you?'

She shook her head, no. 'Did I get sick?'

'A little.'

'Oh.' She moved her hand so it brushed against mine. 'Sorry.'

If Christopher had wanted me to drag my entire life across the world for him I would have. I would've gotten up every day and waited for him to come home, tidied our apartment and walked to the park to take pictures of the sky. I would've built a whole routine around him if he'd asked. There was nothing worth staying for, as far as I was concerned. Nobody else worth holding.

She was asleep again now. And if the johnny was out there waiting for me, it could keep waiting. I laid there with my index and middle fingers resting in her open palm, trying to match my breathing with hers, as the wood pigeons began to call in the trees outside.

Billy Bones His Fancy—on Tattoos

Joshua Calladine-Jones

In the living-room of the Greater Mancunian red-brick terrace, the TV screen is shining in its plastic box. I am a small boy sitting on the floor, probably rewatching *Yellow Submarine*. A towel wrapped around his waist, in comes a man of only twenty-three years old, round wire-frame glasses notched on his beak, his hairline receding to his ears. He aims for the kitchen, for the pan of spitting eggs. Through the curtains I notice it's raining. Soon he will go to work, driving a van, shifting beer-barrels from pub to pub. On his right arm is a human skull framed against a cannabis leaf, the cranium on fire. The ink on this piece is strong. On his left arm is the image of a bird—a swallow—its head bent in flight, a scroll in its mouth, a man's name written across it. The ink has bled from its outlines. In the scroll, the man's name is his own. The man is my father.

It's night in Plymouth. A film student with an apparatus of pencil and thread, I heat a needle, dip it in ink, spelling: Всё, чем держатся их троны—Дело рабочей руки… ('All on which their thrones rest — is made by the worker's hand') on my left calf. The easiest part of skin to mark is close to the tibia, where the flesh is not padded by muscle or fat (both like vaccinating a cushion with a blunt syringe, the spot of ink hard to direct, lacking firm resistance). The winds of the English Channel are beating against the high window of the student halls. In meticulous, steady stabs, I pattern the letters out of dots, though I don't speak any Russian, and of course, mangle several of the letters. I've been watching Eisenstein, caught in a delirium, a delusion.

In Brooklyn I'm visiting my cousin. Together we make a long walk to a tattoo-parlour on the other side of the borough (exactly where is lost to me), passing under criss-crossed metal railway bridges for the elevated lines on Myrtle Avenue, my head filled with hangover, a man pushing a shopping trolley full of empty cans in front of us, then another, then another, but never the same man. They rattle like the trains overhead. The weather pales, the clouds glow. I notice a dead rat in the gutter, lying on its side, reasonably undamaged, though its fur has dried like gelled hair, matted and clumped. My cousin just declared offhand that New York City is its cleanest in years after a huge push from the city council, but here it is: rattus norvegicus, like an image of the plague. Later, the dead animal is added to the design on my shoulder.

A prolonged act of bodily harm, of self-vandalism, I'm tempted to argue for it as the most extreme form of popular visual art, and the most disposable. No other form of illustrative practice is so obviously doomed to loss, to decay, to death, to the brevity of a human lifespan. And even so, the craft is often strongly tethered to tradition: designs and styles are handed down, imitated and adapted by generations of artists, with each prior oeuvre disappearing into the grave. Unless preserved by photography, some other visual art, or, least tangible of all, written description, nowhere else does the artist more or less throw away their labour. Few tattooed bodies have ever been taxidermied, or (more morbidly) skinned. Why practice such folly? Out of sadism? Dandyism? Desperation? And yet for no other form does the subject necessarily suffer more than the artist.

The officer in Kafka's eponymous penal colony understands this, spending hours studying the death agonies of the prisoners that his near-obsolete apparatus tattoos, until he can almost comprehend that, by the last moment, they reach a sort of divine ecstasy of self-comprehension, a nirvana. 'Es ist ein eigentümlicher Apparat,' he claims. A peculiar device indeed. When, as his last request, the officer mounts the apparatus himself, I've often felt that the irony of his death by botched procedure was more aesthetic than moral, having already gone too far in watching the deaths of his prisoners, having come too close to the moment of bliss. The officer tries, but ultimately the tattoo fanatic ends up with a (bad) lethal tattoo.

I'm only fourteen or fifteen when my cousin comes to visit us in England, decked out in his leather jacket, his thick hair cut short: a verified punk. He's come to stay in the old semi-detached, only recently mortgaged by my mother (my father is no longer around). My cousin wants to see Manchester in all its post-industrial glory, to see where we live, to see where his family came from. An emaciated, creeping figure he explains is Max Schreck in *Nosferatu* adorns his right bicep. On the other, the bust of a gilded robotic woman before a resplendent city: the robot Maria from *Metropolis*. But the crowning achievement is about to be displayed: the names of his two best friends, hand-poked on his left and right buttocks. It's hard to tell if this is an act of life-as-prank, or life-as-art.

Pulling the rubber gloves onto her hands, sterilising the needles, cleaning and shaving the area of operation, in a room decorated with framed images, textbook examples all along the walls: here is the tattoo-artist as doctor, surgeon, scientist, creating a form of natural camouflage or adornment, a style of spots and stripes, redefining the bodily patterns on display. She brandishes the tattoo-gun, itself an adaptation of Thomas Edison's defunct electric-pen of 1876. Is this a likely image? A possible one? I can't think of a gallery that shows the painting: *At The Tattoo Studio*, with the artist in a dim daylit room, her subject splayed out on the leather bed before her, as in the famed Rembrandt. His 1632 work, *The Anatomy Lesson of Dr Nicolaes Tulp*, shows the corpse laid out before the doctor as the eager students of the class observe. The left forearm, just dissected, is held slightly aloft, just as (in this imagined painting) the one receiving the tattoo would stretch out their own arm, as in curious awe, the fellow tattooers look on.

This image exists almost exactly in literature, though, if not in figurative, painted art; it comes from a wearer of tattoos himself, Thom Gunn, in his poem, 'Blackie, The Electric Rembrandt', from his debut collection of 1962:

> We watch through the shop-front while
> Blackie draws stars – an equal
>
> concentration on his and
> the youngster's faces. The hand

is steady and accurate;
but the boy does not see it

for his eyes follow the point
that touches (quick, dark movement!)

a virginal arm beneath
his rolled sleeve: he holds his breath.

Gunn is there, holding our hands, holding the boy's hand, each seven-syllable line stabbing, stinging with a clear bright image. Watching together, we're all in the tribe now, all of us equal. And why else wear a tattoo? The boy's innocence, the enormity of possible fates that lie ahead of him, is symbolised with such obviousness, with such indelible design—the pattern of stars.

[He] leaves with a bandage on
his arm, under which gleam ten

stars, hanging in a blue thick
cluster. Now he is starlike.

At some point, I become possessed by a spirit, a neurosis. I spend generous sums at tattoo studios from New York to Manchester to Prague to Plymouth and Leeds, beyond my less-than-modest bank-balance should permit. Weekend jobs in second-hand shops. Greasy café kitchens at the land's edge. Hours editing disturbing video for a certain German painter. And when money is short, I continue on my own leg. What's clear as an outline is that I am trying to emulate *something*, but that something does not have an object yet, does not have a form.

There are many tattooers who regard me with a mixture of pity and perplexity, who, at the end of a near-wordless two-hours-or-so, with only the overheard music and conversations echoing through the studio, will always tell me the cost with a cheerfully relieved expression, though I then trouble them with the confession that I didn't bring enough cash. These are the sort of places that don't generally accept card, meaning that, their expression twisting, they direct me with a single hand to the ATM, out of the damp alleys, out of the side-streets where these studios are always found, towards the oblivious lights of train stations, of shopping malls. This is only for me to return with the promised funds, to be told they'll knock a good fifty quid off the bill, for the virtue of being young and fogged with joy and pain, as they were once.

These are lonely days, where prospects seem misleading and illusory, and the nation austere. Therefore I want something real: a family, a collective. This feeling evolves, ensnares, becomes addictive. It has all of the hallmarks of withdrawal: the remorse, the desire for *better*, for *more*. It's a marriage to a ghost, an abusive husband, instructing me to imitate something that doesn't yet exist. 'Je me ferai des entailles par tout le corps, je me tatouerai'—says Rimbaud's infernal bridegroom to his titular *Vierge Folle*. And there's some similar wish in this directionless desire: to grovel, to howl, to rave. To disfigure myself by some primitive and esoteric method. But only on paper, on skin, in dreams. Hesitant to do anything radical with this hysteria, I direct it at my flesh (ironic, too, my fixation with needles, with ink, like a pen, not brave enough to face the real and transgressive narcotic escape). I want a unification of symbols: a hagiography of tattooed saints.

Here is a woman. The photograph shows her sitting astride a motorbike, clutching the curved handlebars, her eyes the point that draws me into the picture, not letting me avert my eyes. How tired she looks behind her circular shades, the rings heavy in her ears. She's facing away, about to leave, but allowing us the grace of half-turning to look in our direction. On her muscular back is the sweeping design of a koi fish, swimming under a row of flowers (roses? chrysanthemums? the latter the more imperial choice, the flower of the rising sun). Her hair is bleached and shaved. This is transgressive novelist Kathy Acker, known for *Blood and Guts in High School*, *Great Expectations*, and thus symbolic of revolt. Was she aware that Winston Churchill's mother had a snake tattooed around her lower arm in the early twentieth-century, when tattooing became fashionable in the European upper-classes? That Czar Nicholas II wore a dragon? Dragons and snakes, on the crests of nations and biker gangs alike: these emblems of rebellion always possess a character of power.

Here is a man. An Eton-boy with dark blue dots on his knuckles, suspected a communist, an outcast. In Burma he would experience the far-flung boredom, bigotry and callousness of the empire. There, tattoos were thought to protect the wearer from the bullets of the British, and the bites of snakes. There, a person would be formed: Eric Arthur Blair would return to England George Orwell. His act of rebellion, his knuckle-tattoos, were a counter-insignia, signifying—what?—his own independence in leaving the colonial police? Or the need for the independence of the colonies? Perhaps both. There must be something in the ink on Orwell's knuckles that explains the paradoxes in his writing, the doublethink. But it might be impossible to decipher, reduced as it is to one long ellipsis.

What images return from my night of tattooing in the student halls (it was more than one night) are brightened by Eisenstein's *Стачка*, or *Strike* glowing on the laptop screen, having sought it out in the annals of the internet. When I recall it, even the image of cattle slaughtered, of the workers massacred, is blurry (somewhere a rusted hook on a factory floor, somewhere workers fighting, somewhere a charge of men and women) as if the ink of these memories was needled too deep with time: blown-out.

It was this act of stick and poke which Jean Genet, condemned to his cell and conjuring the manuscript of *Notre-Dame-des-Fleurs* on a brown paper bag in 1942, would imagine in the form of the kid-prisoners at the Colony for Child Correction, pricking each other in the night with inked pins. 'La grande occupation nocturne'? Making tattoos:

> The signs were barbaric, full of meaning as are the most barbarous
> signs: of pansies, of bows, of hearts pierced, dripping with blood, of faces
> one atop the other, of stars, of moon-crescents, of contours, of arrows,
> of swallows, of serpents, of boats, of triangular daggers and of inscriptions,
> of mottos, of warnings, all a literature prophetic and terrible.

S asks me to tattoo her arm. She isn't the first to request this, the others (two boys) study at the same art school as me in Plymouth. She also studies there, but in a lower year. Her request is for a cloud, a small rain cloud, on her right bicep. There's no way I'm qualified to do this, I tell her, standing outside the concrete front of the design building, but laughing, she insists. She comes over to the house on the cobbled street near the harbour (I no longer live in the student halls) wearing a faux-fur coat, her hair cropped short. I prepare the needle, the ink, the thread, shave her arm, clean it with hand-sanitiser, draw a design with a fineliner pen. She sits on the yellow bedspread. The naked floorboards groan. As we get ready, I smoke anxiously—though I quit several months ago—excessively tapping the ash to the very stub. S is expressionless, seeming much less on edge than I am, my throat too dry to speak. We begin. But it's only as I'm halfway through the first curve of the cloud that I remember how much younger she is than me. I feel a pain in my chest. It's too late to stop now, the design has to be finished. She's a fashionable, independent girl; I don't want to embarrass her. She already has another done by a friend: a little red wine bottle on the same arm. She's come to me because she knows the Eisenstein story. Does it hurt? I ask. No, she says. We take a break. She smokes from the bedroom window. I do not have the strength, bravery or audacity to be a tattoo-artist.

At the age of twelve or thirteen, my maternal grandfather lends me some of his favourite books: a few Jules Verne, including *Twenty Thousand Leagues*; a biography of the Beatles in Hamburg; and two Robert Louis Stevenson: *The Strange Case of Dr Jekyll and Mr Hyde* and *Treasure Island*. After years of playing games of pirates in his garden, I finally understand the meaning in offering me 'the black spot'.

'But what is the black spot, captain?' I asked.
'That's a summons, mate. I'll tell you if they get that. But you keep your weather-eye open, Jim, and I'll share with you equals, upon my honour.'

It's this place, this garden, across the way from the old limestone quarry of Buxworth, divided into hedged layers and glum woods that taper off far beyond the limits of my grandfather's bungalow, where I was first introduced to the black spot. In its detail—the stream that ran at the foot of the garden after a drop; the canal that ran from the country to the city; the ruins of the quarry—I can see the scene and my grandfather's mock-horrified expression. But the black spot is more than a game, as Jim comes to know all too well. It is already the ultimate objective of tattooing: the inescapable stain, the blank mark of coming doom. Memento Mori made material, given substance in flesh.

In *Treasure Island*, when Billy Bones is examined by the doctor at the Admiral Benbow Inn, such tattoos are revealed: 'A fair wind' and 'Here's luck'. And then there's the image on his shoulder: a man hung from the gallows. All plain sailing so far. But there's another. It's an unusual phrase: 'Billy Bones his fancy'. His fancy—who? It seems to demand signification, to allude to a secret. On one side of this tattooed message stands Billy Bones, veteran pirate, buccaneer coward pursued by Blind Pew. On the other side of the message: the tattooer. It exists in two parts. *Here* is Billy Bones, the man himself. *There*: his fancy. His longing. His desire. Is this, then, an envoi, a message from a shipmate (some kind of reminder or inside joke); a captain (an honour bestowed, a debt marked out); or a lover? (addressed, of course, to: Billy Bones, from: His Fancy). Somewhere between the tattooer and Billy Bones has passed the meaning of these words, and therefore the notion of Billy Bones's desire. Treasure, lust, rum, or some other more or less obscure object. But, granted it's not an abstraction, what image does this refer to? The gallows on his shoulder? Or the act of tattooing itself? Then—*his fancy*—may even be a phrase spelt phonetically without apostrophe (Billy Bones's fancy). In which case, it's no different from any other tattoo. He wears it to remind himself of what he wants.

In the living room of the red-brick house, the blank screen of the television ominous in the corner by the window, I am a boy sitting on the sofa, eating his dinner. Over my head is hung a print of Kandinsky's watercolour circles, warmth and cold overlapping. I enjoy it because it seems like a game, fun shapes painted on the canvas. Bandages wrapped around his arms, a man in a forest-green polo shirt enters, removes his denim Red Sox baseball cap, looking nervously into the hanging mirror above the mantelpiece. Under his hat he is completely bald, light curving over the skin. The round wire-frame glasses are absent, contact-lenses in their place. My mother, with her paints and cut-up magazines splayed out on the table before her, begins asking the expected questions: did it hurt? How will it heal? Can we see? This is one of the last memories I will have of my father at the house. With an oddly clinical indifference, my mother watches him remove the bandages. Underneath, the old tattoos are gone. I look closely. New ones, thick, black and blank, are marked in their place.

FEATURED POET

Alicia Byrne Keane holds a BA in English Literature and French from Trinity College Dublin and a MSt. from Oxford University, and is finishing an Irish Research Council-funded PhD thesis at TCD. Alicia's poetry has appeared in *The Moth, The Colorado Review, The Berkeley Poetry Review*, and *Banshee*, among others. Alicia's poem 'surface audience' was nominated for the Pushcart and Best of the Net prizes; Alicia is in receipt of an Irish Arts Council Agility Award.

In the brand new silence

I am being sewn to the sea: the sting of the jab
a bright column, buoying me up. I both feel
and don't feel that anticipated mesh—
a roomful of people my exact age, like school.
Clothes go fluorescent in shadow like this,
a clutch of glows. Someone's lemon-pale halter top,
white sneakers crossed under a chair.
The heatwave's end postponed each time I check
my phone. In a previous, precious endlessness
plum trees bordered the house, seemed a reminder:
a careful hand digging the beds. The barn would make
the roadside a fiction, I would never walk beyond
the rusting trough—water-spiders ruched its teal silk.
There's a way things light up sometimes.
The roof tiles were a sear of sun on shallows,
seemed to take flight. I am back here, painless,
only waiting for cloud-cover to roll in.

Egg

I keep a list of coincidences in my phone
like I can cloud the glow of rarities, try
to make the threat leap out of an object
via its flattest side—reconnection a thing
tea-lit, a tiny eye in the smoke-dark bulb
of a keepsake, the startle of ceramic. Maybe
this is why people draw: fix the luminous
where it curls and shivers. For the time
being I am just concerned with igneous
weights and the issue of their settling.
Earlier, rib-propped, the dune of the
couch, this very expectant apartment.
A cold dart of a thing underfoot, a whole
solidness waning. I thought: this will
be something very unpleasant. This will
be a stilled pour or blade. But it was only a
capo, birdlike: I often try to make them
snap sleek, but they are always crotchety
and disappointing. Stiff hand, I imagine
rain in your image, metal weights on
rooftops hammering everything smooth.

Sunset Synonym

The room absorbing a solstice:
I dream unknown swathes
moss or breath, noon
dimmed by leaves.

The room full of boxes in the dark:
a path becomes cobweb, migraine
swollen with dirty light. I spend
this introduction furrowed.

The room, a moment reaching warmth:
we extend infinitely. Starts, starlings
flit granular ahead, our vision
sharp as beaks.

The room: yet more fizzled things
settling into a truce,
a shallow hum of cells. I think
of the rift as glossy, new.

The room, all I want:
a whorl of rest linen scented.
I measure nightfall by the boiler's rush—
our pause is woven, a good place to curl.

The room a blistered rise:
kettle noise fixing us in a tightness.
I can't go about my business
in the morning's held gaze.

The room records our stances:
the sigh where luminescence tilts.
Here at the sink like clock hands.
Here at the sinking, cloistered.

Sapindale

I slice an interruption in the side of this room:
I have forgotten to turn off the main light,
calm the island of its wire-ridged skin. Now
it meets sun here at the meekest part of the
ceiling, where two peach-slivered saturations
coil. There is only one letter between water
and waver, everything lit from the wrong place.
If you saw this nervous palm from a distance,
shucked from the rooms around it, unstacking
would sway you. Into a terrible bluntness, a
swoon—it could be any time of year right now.
The orange you left on my bedside table is
missing a river of rind. I think my way into
several underpinnings, the fibrous paper of
midday & the place where veins cling. The
ripped parts look like seafoam, and I always
forget stage-fainting is all too easy, knees
hinged to speak recline as mermaids on rocks.

MBARI soundscape

listening room

When we resubmerge ourselves
the silence has developed layers,
flint-hard facets. Our darkness
falls away and this could be
windblown grass, bird-chatter.
(I try to   remember how water
is   meant to be   pressing   around
us,   I try to   remember water   at
all,   it's been so long since   I have
let a   seaside expand   itself in my
chest.) I give the noise a stubborn
overground shape, wildflower-
crushed valleys. This trill could be
sonar could be violins   could be
my own ear's pink light-inflated
insides   could be sun-bleached
dog-toys in the garden could be
cadmium yellow   could be spring
lengthening across us through
the windows   but we are still
entrenched. How do I narrate
when the recording has dropped
away, the sea an eye blinking
shut?

Algae

In my dream where the wrack swathed us
we had just left somewhere pebble-dashed
& brassy with heat inside: spark-flit hearth
full of tiny breakages. I remember a splinter
catching in wool, bare floorboards, clutches
of beer bottles in the door's shadow. Last
night I held the unthinkable, planned my
way through all the disasters I could. When
embers make a shower sometimes a word
retains itself within a closed eyelid: here.
Hush, flora, scum. I, soot, granite, heave.
Acceptance a footprint filling slowly with
silt; me, loving wholly even as fronds slip
between us & an immensity opens in my
left ear, the one that always pops. It's been
sand-whorled until now, this winter, it's
been real (hair in salted twists blood-sharp),
& the next sliver of strand you visit will be
gifted an autumn, love russet & abounding.

Earthenware

after Györgi Petri

now only clay
now only wet hands
now only clay meeting wet hands on this wheel
now only intention and touch

now only elbows anchored tightly against body
now the fragrance of clay

evokes memories of my foremothers:
you slipped away one day in midsummer, returned to the soil

now only this dance
the clay rises like Lazarus
now only anticipation
what character will this clay take?
now only a vase
for the cosmos

Maria Fitzgerald

Detrition

We are down to the roots and nodes,
even the underlayers of skin worn away
and rocks lifted out—so tunnel vision
in the broken valley, so local in our
references. Down to the bare bones
of spectre-selves, trying to make repairs
where run-off has sluiced through dryness,
rolling then untopping then gouging
faster even than high-summer tree-death.
Everywhere, we've eroded, each regional
inflection, each point of repair snapshotted
and collated, expecting a long-lasting view
as we truncate then consign ourselves,
or kinsfolk do, or laws and bylaws will,
to ensure detrition doesn't move us about
too much, make us eerily worldly.

John Kinsella

The Goose Harvest

Jodie Wray

I

This morning I watched a man empty the ward's payphone. And I realised my assumptions about where the coins go in a payphone had been all wrong.

I had always imagined they dropped down into the body of the phone itself, completing a circuit which allows you to go ahead and talk. The inner workings of the phone would digest them gradually—mechanically—via some series of cogs, chutes and clockwork until the end of the paid-for time. Then the coins would roll away, breaking the connection, and leaving the phone to announce its renewed hunger with the pips.

So I'd been looking forward to seeing a payphone opened and autopsied.

But all the phone guy did was use a key to open a metal panel I hadn't noticed before underneath the phone, and pull out a plastic box of money. White plastic, yellowing a bit. Like old Tupperware.

I said to him I had always supposed the coins stayed in the belly of the phone and he said people always think that.

I wondered how many phones the phone guy has to empty each day. I didn't ask him though, in case it just sounded like politely feigned interest. Which was stupid because I was actually genuinely interested. And he was unlikely to feel patronised by someone in here. Probably thinking to himself *poor cow*.

II

Addictions units are less boring for me than for most patients. Or at least by now I soon acclimatise to the boredom.

I was in a place once where the patients were so bored that, one day, they took all the plastic stackable chairs out of the dining-room and arranged them into a chair-pyramid in the smoking-yard outside. It was just something to do. Not a protest or anything.

And this time I have been sent into the countryside for my re-education.

This ward has two television rooms, a ping-pong table, a payphone, a vending-machine for snacks, an exercise-bike that nobody uses, and a cupboard full of jigsaws and some art materials (but no paper).

By now I can tell which of the other patients has been in prison, and for how long, by how good they are at ping-pong. I can tell if a woman patient has been on the game, because she will talk about her kids having been taken into care, but she won't say anything about hoping to get them back.

And even if I couldn't infer any of this, someone will always come out of the weekly AA or NA meetings (attendance is optional, so I've opted out) and tell me Absolutely Everything Everybody Who Isn't Them has shared in it.

For the first five days in here I had to go after dinner to be hooked up to a vitamin-drip that made my sweat smell like soup. The liquid in the drip was straw-coloured, so it looked like I was being refilled from a bag of piss.

'Some pop stars actually *pay* to get this done before they go on tour!' said the nurse brightly, glad to be away from the noise of the ward in that broom-cupboard of an examination room.

One of the other patients getting a drip had skin as yellow as the fluid draining into him. Liver failing. My liver tests came back showing damage, but it's still reversible so I'm lucky. The first stage of serious damage is when the liver gets fatty, like foie gras.

III

I've brought a book in with me that you gave me years ago. *Life: A User's Manual* by Georges Perec. I hadn't got around to reading it before now, and I thought a long book would help pass the time.

It's a bit of a let-down. I think you're supposed to see something to do with jigsaws, or chess—whatever—in its structure. I'd rather have a real jigsaw, to be honest. I've started doing them since I came in here. And they are pretty good for distracting myself.

I'm beginning to know if a jigsaw will be any good from the brand name on the box. A quality jigsaw is made of thick card and the pieces slot into each other with a pleasing click. Cheap jigsaws use flimsy card and the pieces aren't cut cleanly enough to fit back together properly—the more of the picture you complete, the more it buckles up and cracks apart, like the crust on a lava-flow.

The jigsaw I'm working on at the moment is a picture of Carnaby Street in the 1960s. A drawing, not a photograph. There's a man in the centre of it riding a Vespa and wearing a T-shirt which says *The Who*. That's the bit I'm saving to complete last. I think it's good to end on a question.

Sometimes, when I'm undressing for bed at night, stray jigsaw pieces that have been sticking to my clothes all day flutter down to the floor, like tiny lobed moths.

IV

When, along with seven of our friends, I received your round-robin email headed, News from Brussels!, I thought it was going to contain a joke about Brexit or football or something. That was once I'd got over the shock of hearing from you at all.

But instead it said: 'Hi all, I'm going to be a father! Aurélie & I are expecting a baby girl in November. She'll be half-French, half-English, and born in Belgium, so I hope she doesn't grow up too confused! Seriously though—I'm delighted.'

So I clicked 'reply all' and wrote: 'Congratulations—wonderful news!'

Then I went out to the off-licence for the first time in eighteen months. I bought two bottles of mid-price Rioja and a half-bottle of whisky. And then I called a dealer for the first time in eighteen months and bought a gram of cocaine.

Later that night I wrote an email which was to you, and you alone. It said: 'Fuck you and fuck your French bitch. I hope she and your fucking brat both die.'

V

One of the advantages of being in a hospital in the country is that you can go out for walks. Or one walk a day anyway. Not on your own obviously. A nurse accompanies us. Some of the nurses enjoy the walk and some don't. Last Saturday it was Jyoti, an agency nurse from India. I think she probably feels neutral about it. Like all the nurses she ignores the fact that once we're out of sight of the ward half the group light up fags, even though the hospital grounds are supposed to be No Smoking.

Stuartie had been admitted to the ward for alcohol detox three days before, so he was still on Librium until the danger of seizures had passed. He seemed to fancy himself as a bit of a lady-killer with the nurses. Maybe it's because he was so high on the Librium. Or maybe he's just a twat.

'Josie, what do you do on your days off? Is it alright if I call you Josie?'

'You can call me Jyoti. My name is Jyoti.'

'Sure I can't say that. I'll just call you Josie. So what do you do on your days off anyhow, Josie?'

'You can say it. It's easy. Jee-Oh-Tee. And I spend most of my days off cleaning up after my husband and kids.'

I was sick of listening to Stuartie, so I went on ahead and stood by the wall at the edge of a ploughed field, dragging on my cigarette. Some days there are rabbits in that field. If the nurses are bored they clap their hands to startle them, and the rabbits run off in different directions, little white tails bobbing and flashing against the dark earth.

I noticed something on the ground just beyond the wall. Round and white, so at first I thought it was a football, only it was too small. Gemma from Scotland came over to see what I was staring at. Then Jyoti and the others caught up with us.

I said: 'I think it's a puffball.'

And Gemma said: 'Yes, it must be.'

And Jyoti asked: 'What is a puffball?'

And I said: 'It's like a mushroom.'

And Jyoti asked: 'Is it a magic mushroom? What does a magic mushroom look like?'

I told her magic mushrooms look like little skinny mushrooms. Nothing like this, which is a puffball.

Jyoti was still eyeing me, unconvinced, when the space behind us was suddenly filled with noise. Clashing, metallic, harsh, uncanny, almost-voices, almost-human. As immediate and intense as if someone had flung open a soundproofed door, to reveal there was an ancient battle raging on the other side.

Looking up, we saw a flock of geese overhead. So high up they were just dark specks, like cinders carried on the air. They seemed much too far above us to be shattering every bit of the distance between us and them with their cries, so loud they penetrated like audible shrapnel.

There's a lough somewhere round here. I suppose that's where they were heading.

On the walk the next day the puffball had vanished.

VI

The collective noun for a group of geese actually looks like geese itself. Look: 'gaggle'. In lowercase the three 'g's are like a row of three little geese. Fat bodies with a head at the end of a thin neck. There's even the suggestion of a beak if you're using a serif font. I wouldn't know what a serif font was if you hadn't told me. You were quite into your fonts.

In film and television drama you know the period-setting is the Middle Ages as soon as you see a shot of a flock of geese being driven across some ploughed earth by a peasant. The geese function as a visual historical synecdoche that orients you. It's called an establishing shot.

I tried explaining that to you the first night we met, at Matt's party. I had told you I was a script editor on a TV series about a monk who was also a detective in medieval England.

You said: 'I'm a statistician in the Civil Service.'

And I asked: 'So, is there safety in numbers, then?'

And you laughed.

Within a month we'd found a flat with a shared garden to rent on Denmark Hill. Home for the next four years. Camberwell was always good value, you said. Cheap because it's not on the Tube.

VII

In here I wake up at 3.45 am on the dot every morning and get up and go to the toilet. I'm sharing a room with another woman, so I open the door slowly and gently so as not to wake her. Outside everything is dark apart from the light in the nurses' office, which has a huge window looking out on the ward.

On admission you're taken in there and the nurses search through your belongings. They take your phone, which is placed in a Ziploc bag labelled with your name and the date and then shut away in a safe. First-timers often aren't expecting this. The younger ones reel out of the office afterwards looking as dazed as sudden amputees.

Throughout the night patients will shuffle up to the office window and tap on the glass to get the nurses' attention. Usually they want something to help them sleep. The nurses will say no, and the patients will shuffle off again. But they'll keep coming back every hour or so. It's the heroin addicts mostly, because they itch a lot and it's worse at night. In the morning some of their forearms are scratched raw. Little Zoe has a sore on one of hers that won't heal and needs a proper dressing; she says she got it from gear she bought off a Russian.

When I was coming back from the toilet at 3.51 am this morning, the nurses in the office tapped on the glass and beckoned me over. They were laughing because a nurse on duty the night before had thought I was a ghost when she saw me going past in my white nightdress.

'The rest of them are all in their pyjamas. But you look very, um...Wuthering Heights!'

And when I was back in bed I found myself wondering what it would be like to be a ghost, and to haunt somewhere.

Lonely, probably; certainly repetitive.

And if a ghost is haunting somewhere, but there is no one alive around to see it doing the haunting, does that still count? Or is that like asking whether a tree falling over in a forest makes a sound, when there is categorically and definitely nobody around to hear it?

VIII

If someone were to ask me how often I think about you, the answer I'd give would be 'often'. Because that sounds better than 'all the time'.

Like yesterday when I was in Group, sitting in a squat leatherette armchair while Neil the social worker got us to list our *Top 10 Trigger Situations to Avoid*, and I noticed that Little Zoe was removing bits of her hair. Up went her hands to the back of her head, and down they came, clutching fistfuls of long blonde locks.

Hair extensions. I'm surprised she had the patience to clip them in in the first place.

She laid them out carefully along the arm of her chair. And once she had finished with her hair, she reached into her mouth and took out the braces from her teeth and placed them beside the hair. Then she resumed writing in her pink glittery notebook with her outsized fun-pen which had a plastic unicorn dangling from it on a cord.

And I remembered how once you and I followed a trail of hair extensions scattered all the way down Denmark Hill. They were on the pavement, so whoever dropped them must have been on foot. Had they been running away from somebody? Had they robbed a hairdresser's and fled down the hill? Past the Maudsley Hospital, past the people waiting at bus-stops and past the huddles of schoolkids staring at their phones? And then on through the crowds of shoppers—past Edwardes Cycles, past Nando's and McDonalds, and on towards Camberwell Green, all the while shedding stolen hair—blonde, red, brunette—behind them?

It was around that time that I started having trouble sleeping. So I would stick in my earbuds and listen to audiobooks of Sherlock Holmes stories while you slept beside me. My favourite was *The Adventure of the Blue Carbuncle*. In it a thief hides a stolen jewel by feeding it to one of the geese his sister is raising in a yard at 117 Brixton Road.

I always enjoyed the bit where Holmes declares the bird 'a *most unimpeachable* Christmas goose'. The goose was blameless. Anyone could see that. You didn't have to be Sherlock Holmes to see that the goose had done nothing to reproach itself with.

And one Sunday, when we couldn't think of anything else to do, I suggested we walk to Brixton Road and find out if the location of the goose-yard in the story still existed.

When we got there, No. 117 turned out to be part of a genteel terrace, Grade II Listed. Not the sort of place to raise poultry in, but pretty enough to look at. And lucky in that part of London to have escaped the V-1 attacks towards the end of the war. Flying bombs. Doodlebugs. Germany's 'Vengeance Weapons'.

We spent the rest of that afternoon down the pub. I was on soda water and lime. And later we had what must have been—looking back now—one of our last ten fucks. Maybe even our last five. Or maybe it was just the last one when we were both happy.

IX

If a goose happened to be sitting in a pub around closing time, or maybe was on the other side of the room at a party, where it's dark, someone might well go up to it thinking it was a swan. Maybe because they've had a few drinks themselves, and so are feeling bold enough to go up to a swan.

Only, once they get close enough, they realise, too late, that it is a goose and melancholy they are getting. It was a swan they were expecting. And a fine pliant swan at that, the sort that nuzzles its bill down into its powderpuff of a breast, simpering and agreeable.

A swan's neck might curve back like a question-mark, but it's a question-mark which is there purely for show. They don't question anything. The stupid things only start to sing once they realise they're dying.

Geese have necks as straight as periscopes, because a goose knows it needs to be on the lookout.

Sad, clever goose. Watchful, ancient goose. Practical bird, of which every part can be used except for the honk. Flesh for meat, feathers for pillows, quills for pens.

The cries of the sacred geese on the Capitoline Hill alerted the Romans when Gauls tried to invade Rome. Geese thereby saved the city. But even after that, geese had to keep their guard up. Some cruddy soothsayer could always be lurking in the background, ready to cut a goose open and tell the future from its liver.

My liver has started issuing warnings about the future too. But there's nothing like trying to change. Again.

X

A woman about my age comes in on Wednesdays to teach us Mindfulness-Based Stress Reduction. I quite enjoy it. I've done it before, so I know not to just eat the raisin as soon as she hands it out to you. You've got to eat it slowly, while paying attention, non-judgmentally, and in the moment.

Mindfulness Woman is fond of what you might call 'quirky' jewellery. Big, bright necklaces like Lego bricks strung together; armfuls of Perspex bangles and friendship bracelets; earrings not totally matching, but riffing on the same theme—a crescent moon dangling on one side, a shooting star on the other.

Whenever I see 'quirky' jewellery, I know I am in the presence of a Natural Enemy.

I can tell she dislikes me too. Because last Wednesday she took such evident pleasure in telling me how *worried* she was that I always looked *just so unhappy*. It was clear to her that I was an intelligent person. She wondered if I liked reading.

I did not say: 'I am indeed an intelligent person, and my resting face is (so I've been told) *farouche.*'

Instead I said: 'Yes, I do like reading. I did English and Drama at university, years ago.'

So this week, Mindfulness Woman presented me with a page of inspirational quotes from the writings of a famous Zen Buddhist monk. She told me that every year she spends a week at this famous monk's International Retreat Village in the Dordogne. It sounds like some sort of Butlin's For Buddhists. I could see she had printed the quotes off from a Mindfulness website, perhaps even her own. Next to them was a stock photo of a stack of pebbles. Stock photos of this type are often employed to suggest a Zen sensibility by people who design Mindfulness websites.

Designers of Mindfulness websites never use the famous photo of the Zen monk Thich Quang Duc meditating in the lotus position, and every bit as still and pyramidal as a stack of pebbles, as he burned himself to death on a street in Saigon. I guess it's just not their kind of thing.

XI

Neil the social worker says this ward feels homely—not like some of the other places he's worked in. There are pictures on the walls here for a start. In fact the pictures are all prints of works by Van Gogh, apart from the one next to the nurses' office, which is a Rothko. Paintings by suicides on the walls of a mental hospital? Somebody must have been having a laugh.

Maybe I should write online reviews of the addictions units I've been in. I'm sure there's a market for it.

'Five stars. Can't fault this place if, as I did at the time of my stay, you have private health insurance through your job. Although after my stay I relapsed immediately, thus ending access to both job and health insurance. Trains from Paddington on the quarter-hour.'

'Three stars. Run by Quakers in Yorkshire. Rains a lot. All chocolate in the vending-machine is certified Fairtrade.'

'One star. NHS ward in outer London. Understaffed. Cans of Special Brew are cynically piled next to the till in the petrol-station opposite the hospital, ready for the day you are discharged.'

Nothing wrong with having a Tripadvisor for Addicts. A *Rough Guide*? A *Lonely Planet*?

Yes. It is.

Neil the social worker said it is good that I go out for the walk every day. He would do it more himself if he had the time. Sometimes it helps to be out in nature, to feel part of something bigger.

But what I love about nature is that it's utterly indifferent to me. I love that the geese neither know nor care that their cries could stop a ragbag of drunks, cokeheads and junkies dead in their tracks beside a blank field in Ireland in autumn. Those geese might have sounded like a skyful of avenging angels, but it's alright. They passed us over. They're not coming for us. Not yet.

XII

In the last addictions unit in London there was a phone, but it only allowed incoming calls. One patient was fresh out of prison, where he'd undergone a religious conversion. But he was still juggling three girlfriends (one pregnant) on the outside, and if the phone rang he'd sprint towards it. Be on it for hours sometimes.

I had been in there for four days when they told me I had a visitor. Of course I thought it was you. A nurse led me into a room which smelt of Febreze, where two huge IKEA sofas faced each other. Space for any number of concerned relatives. I wasn't expecting to see your brother there.

'Is Dan parking the car?' I asked.

'Dan's not here,' said your brother. 'He tried to get through on the phone, but it was always engaged. He's in Brussels.'

'Why? Did they need him early or something?'

'He's there now.'

'But his secondment doesn't start until August. I can't go out there yet.'

'He didn't say anything in case it stopped you from coming in here. And he wants you to get better. He really, *really* wants you to get better. But he said he can't do this anymore.'

'Do what?'

'He didn't feel it would be fair to tell you until you were safe. In here. With people around you. I'm sorry. You don't need to leave the flat yet. You can stay until you get back on your feet. He'll keep paying his half of the rent. There'll still be three months left on the lease when you get out of here.'

But I didn't get back on my feet. I lay on the floor for months instead. You'd changed your number, blocked me on Facebook. On email too, I assumed; or at least you never replied.

By the time the lease was up in August I'd stopped answering my own phone altogether. My sister was so worried she came over from Belfast to get me. She cleaned the flat up. Got rid of any evidence. I think I overheard her saying something apologetic to one of the neighbours at some point. Meanwhile I was outside, lying on my back in the shared garden, staring at the sky.

Once, in Ireland long ago, a hunter was about to shoot a flock of geese flying overhead. But a priest stopped him. 'Those geese are the souls of people who left Ireland and died before they could return,' said the priest. Now they couldn't fail to return, every year.

I've never liked that story and think it would have been a mercy if the hunter had shot them dead there and then. Broken the repetition. Set them free from an eternity spitted on the hands of the clock. And what was an Irish priest doing believing in reincarnation anyway?

XIII

I phoned Matt from the ward a few days ago. Because I had to ask him.

'Has Dan's baby been born yet?'

'I don't know. Haven't heard from him. When was it due? This month?'

'November.'

'So if it had been born now it would be early?'

'If you hear she's been born please will you let me know? Phone the ward payphone. If someone else answers, leave a message saying you want me to call you back.'

'OK.'

'If you hear anything at all. Please, I know this sounds crazy, but I need to know she's alright. Because I told him I hoped she'd die. And now I can't stop thinking that if something bad happens to the baby, it's because I cursed her.'

'Just concentrate on getting better. I'll phone if I hear anything. Promise. Is there anything you need in the meantime?'

'I need to know what the geese that fly over this hospital look like. Could you find out? And send me a picture of them? They're too high up for me to see from the ground.'

XIV

Today a letter came from Matt. A nurse called me into the office to open it in front of her. When I say a letter, it's actually just the printed-out Wikipedia entry for a species of goose. When the nurse saw it she laughed and asked me if I was already thinking about ordering my Christmas dinner. I felt myself wince.

Because a goose always looks so calm, so solemn. Dignified. Stoical even. Like it is not only resigned to its own fate, but that it also feels the weight of the sacrifice of all the preceding generations of geese. It is a far, far better thing, etc. It makes me sad to think of them melted down and put in jars to roast potatoes.

'This goose,' Matt had written on the back of the page, 'is the one most likely to be flying over where you are at this time of year. The greylag goose. Latin name: *Anser anser.*'

It's a beautiful bird. Flame-orange beak; coral legs; grey feathers like knapped flint spearheads.

I've propped the picture of the goose against the lamp on my bedside locker, so I can look at it while I'm waiting to go to sleep.

XV

I dream I'm at the top of Denmark Hill in a chariot. It's the sun-god's chariot—the same one that Medea escapes in at the end of her play. Only while Medea's chariot was pulled by dragons, mine is pulled by two gigantic, majestic, fuck-off geese.

I turn the chariot to face the sun and we start taxiing towards it. As the geese and I lift off from the ground I do struggle a bit to keep hold of the reins, but the geese know where they are going and they don't flinch. We're heading straight towards the sun, and before long our hair and our feathers begin to smoulder.

Five minutes in, and fat from our bodies starts to melt off and fall to earth in great yellow gobbets. It explodes like napalm on impact, burning up everything for miles.

I look ahead at the geese. They are still flying and pulling me on. Only now I can see their rib-bones, exposed and blackening, as their skin shrinks back and shrivels and the flames devour their flesh. Soon they are blazing like twin Hindenburgs.

As for me, I realise that I have long since been turning into metal. I try opening and closing my jaw and I find it is brass. I can feel the pins where it is hinged onto my skull and the spring which snaps it shut.

My skin is a layer of hammered copper and underneath it my cheekbones and nose are steel. My eyes have been boiled away and in their place are red pebbles. Somebody's carved an iris on them, but no pupil.

We fly over a ploughed field far below. And you're down there, sitting at your desk, scrolling through spreadsheets, or reports about Pelagic Fish Stock Assessment, or some other shit I don't give a fuck about.

You hear the cries of my geese and you look up. And your expression turns to one of fear.

Which is how it should be.

Because soon the geese and I are going to slam into the earth with an explosion so almighty it'll send out shockwaves to tear up roads and collapse all buildings.

But for the moment we are circling above you, and I'm shouting down at you and asking you if this is what you wanted? And how could you ever imagine that the loss of love is a trivial grief for a woman?

Answer. Just answer.

One hazard of a messy home

If an inc_mplet_ Scr_bble set
accident_lly joins forces

                                                  with a consummate counterpart,

     it takeS
        E
        V
        E
   Y E A R S
        A
        L

                              uncommonLy
                                  O
                                  N
                                  G

                                            G
                                     M A T C H E S
                                          M
                                          E
                                          S

and s_me v_ry vex_d ev_nts

                         to finally figure out

that the board possesses a S
                          C
                          O
                          R

                          _

                                                _f _iles _oo many.

Clodagh Beresford Dunne

Shape/Colour/Weather

Sarah Maria Griffin

And if you find some day dear friend my sad head upon
  your shoulders
go out into the world and say world it's been so long say world hello

> Stephen Sexton, 'Yoshi's House', *If All The World And Love Were Young*

In the spring of 2018, in the stiff wake of a back injury, I took my first long-distance hike. It was ten days in northern Spain, trekking towards the city of Santiago. The weather was largely grey, some days it rained, and the group I hiked with wore heavy plastic cloaks. In the woods and on the long, dusty roadsides I was as much there on the pilgrimage as I was *in* my body: I remember distinctly being thankful for the cold of the elements on my bare legs, a weird balm against their constant burn.

Towards the end of the route, I discovered as I limped into the day each morning that I was capable of holding the pain that came up through the soles of my feet and into my legs. Pain that I had put there with each mile: bracing, clean, and bright. It felt honest. Good, almost.

This was the first big hike, though I have always been a walker, and since then I have been seeking the feeling that this strain gives to my body and the emptiness that floods my busy head, too. This delicious blank is something I have found before, too—albeit in a different shape.

Though I only began to hike in 2018, I am not a stranger to long, silent pilgrimages through dense green forests and bare, quiet villages. For years I performed this act by proxy, without moving much more of my body than my hands as they input commands to a screen through a controller. Before, it was only ever in the quiet of my home, lit green by the fields on my television, untouched by the rain, by the heat.

***

2017's *The Legend of Zelda: Breath of the Wild* was critically lauded upon release for its ambition, scale, and total realisation of a fictional world which first appeared through grainy pixels in 1986. *Breath* is the story of a young man called Link, awoken after a long sleep, compelled by destiny to rescue the imperiled Princess Zelda from a great beast, the Calamity Ganon. It takes place, as almost all of its predecessors with more or less identical stories do, in a lush, wild land called Hyrule. This place, and this story, has been reiterated again and again as technology has leapt forward. The Hyrules I have visited (first in 1997, while playing *The Ocarina of Time* on the Nintendo 64) have always had a distinct tonal identity, a sense of space conjured by the dimension of the art, the light, the music, the push of a controller, the place where my hand meets the plastic meets the wires meets the screen. There are musical leitmotifs that appear in game after game; non-playable characters who inhabit Hyrule rendered over generations; a colour palette of greens and greys and golds that make up the reality of this place; a bestiary of returning giant spiders, dragons, hands that descend from ceilings. There is a language to this place that I have developed a fluency in through years of immersion.

These components build a sense of reality that is the product of hundreds of people's work and talent. They are not naturally occurring phenomenon, they are deliberate. Every tree, every panel of light that falls between the boughs. Every ripple in the water and blade of swaying grass. The rabbits, the birds, the deer that lope through the plains or the tiny plants that grow, resolute, through deep piles of snow that crunches underfoot.

None of these sensations or details has anything to do with the story of the game, or the function of the quest. In the *Zeldas* I have played since I was a child, I've imagined these details beyond the squareness of pixel and polygon: the shape and colour and weather exist inside a personal landscape, even if in the television there is something much simpler.

I am, in my playing, less inclined towards the destiny the story spins and repeats, and more interested in the act of walking the land. Turning over rocks. Talking to people. Putting fictional distance under the fictional body I am both guiding and tethered to. Experiencing travel, transport—a freedom.

When we talk about video games, a great many of us met them for the first time as children and while their resonance might begin there, it cannot end there, too. I am talking here about my adulthood, as *Breath* was released when I was 29, and I began hiking the following year. I have spent, arguably, solid months of my life in different expressions of this singular idea of Hyrule. So, though I first touched this other place and felt its power as a child, it is as present in my everyday life as any piece of music, any book, any film—any text. Rooting every conversation we have about video games within childhood cements them as toy, before text. The video game can be both things at once.

This tension between toy and text is palpable: we play the text. I would argue that we can also play the video-game-as-text as though it were an instrument—a site of expression and growth, as well as acknowledging its function as a toy. The medium contains multitudes: it gives back to us what we bring to the screen, the fourth wall fluid, while also being a defined, intentional expression by the teams who built it. So, in discussing this location, this Hyrule, I am placed firmly in this duality, attempting to interpret the space as picture, as sculpture, as symphony, without negating its core function and intention: as game. Personally, though, I read and have always read the various *Legends of Zelda* that I have played as though they were books. Not books full of text. Books full of something else.

***

Here are some things Hyrule always has:
   A lake.
   A castle.
   A desert.
   A forest.
   A mountain.
   A princess.
   A long way to walk.
   Often, a graveyard.
   Always, weather.

***

Since walking to Santiago, I made it my mission to take a Big Walk every year. A week, at least, somewhere green, where I can negate all responsibility to anything other than getting a certain amount of kilometers underfoot. I'd always liked walking: favouring walking home from the city after nights out over getting the bus, even if it meant extra hours questing home in the dark. I was notorious for convincing dates to walk the coastline with me rather than going into bars, socialising and often drinking on foot. I like moving with people: the propulsion keeps things interesting, alleviating some of the stress of making conversation. However, trail life is new. The push, the burn, that easy blankness of the head after a day or so, all new, all different.

I recruit my husband; we take a hike or two a year. A week here or there, when we can. They are good, and hard, and his presence with me is special in the quiet rhythm of travel—I think he understands it in the same way I do, isn't bored by it or outraged by my insistence that we do not go to a beach on our holidays, but instead walk two hundred kilometers through rough terrain in Clare.

I would take these walks alone if it weren't so dangerous. I don't mean the rocks, or the distance, or uneven cliffsides. I don't even mean the potential for injury, which looms over me and my soft, city body at all times. We might walk for days and not see another person on a trail, but if I were alone out there, out of signal, I am not so naïve to think that a woman walking alone in the forest is not a target. I seldom think of my gender, other than when I feel afraid in public. Though the forest and hills are so quiet that they do not feel public at all (rather, entirely private, entirely mine), they are not. Even entertaining this fantasy is dangerous.

I am not equipped with any sword, any shield, any fat glass bottles of magic when I am out in the green world. I am an adept warrior with a controller in my hand: I am quick to parry, not afraid of summoning the spirits of the dead to unleash bolts of lightning to survive, partial to a flaming arrow; I have been teaching myself these things, using Link's body—left-handed, like me—since I was twelve years old. However, out there, I simply must take one thing with me to be safe: another person. Preferably, a man.

***

In the dense silence of 2020, we don't leave the house much. But, while we are in the grey and heavy of the indoors and the news cycle, we do play *Breath* from the beginning. Its lush green world is comforting and familiar, but also a stark reminder of all of the walking we cannot do, all of the world we cannot see as we wait out this dark phenomenon. I think almost constantly about the clean pain in my legs, my hips—how badly I want it. About the noise of trees, the empty in my head.

I move Link across Hyrule field, avoiding combat at all costs. I do not take a horse with me, though there are dozens available to ride. I walk his small body by rushing, heavy rivers; I lurk through dappled woodland with my bow, picking off creatures who threaten the peace of my pilgrimage with their programmed, predictable violence. I am not here to fight. I am here to walk.

Hyrule is laid out within this game so that everything you can see, you can touch (if you are clever enough, if you are strong enough, if you have enough stamina and I can have all of those things because I am Link). The story I am telling myself is that he and I are just adventurers. That in order to want to save this world I must walk every pixel of it. That I must touch the invisible boundaries where the game, finally, shows me its limits, and the world just stops. Then I can turn around and resume my quest. I can place my body against the ridge of colour and shape where the world ends and becomes nothing, then I can turn around and continue my walk. This landscape is open and wild, while mine, in reality, in 2020, is sealed shut by the pandemic. There, I have the equipment to face down or evade monstrosity; here, I have nothing.

During the lockdown, when I cannot leave the house, CB is a patient emissary in a mask and I am at my desk, in sweatpants, frozen. My father recovers from Covid. I call my mother three times a day and play video games. I still cannot put a name on what happened to me during that first rush of the pandemic: I largely avoid socialising on the internet because I can't pretend that I am not losing my mind. It is late summer before I am able to confidently walk outside without feeling intense, fluttering horror and wanting more than anything to just go back in and draw the blinds. Most mornings, the furthest I get is my back door, where I stand and look at the enormous roses that somehow grow, hungry, thorned, enormous in the stone yard. I can hardly bring myself to walk another miserable 1,800 footsteps (as noted, diligently by my phone's pedometer) to the Spar and back, by the expensive houses on Bath Avenue. I stand in the bathroom some nights and listen to my neighbours sing through the walls. Ringsend closes in on me.

When we finally move from the dark corridor of a terrace house to another rental outside of the city, we choose the foot of the Dublin Mountains, so that when we walk there is a forest there for us. In the winter, at night, we walk in the woods together with huge floodlight torches and we laugh and we are freezing but we are not afraid.

When the lockdowns of 2021 are alleviated, in midsummer, we immediately borrow a lift two hours down the road—a side effect of being lifelong small-gaff-in-various-city-dwellers means that neither of us can drive. The Wicklow Way is typically walked from Marlay Park to Clonegal, but we—for the second time—decide to begin at the end, and walk back to Dublin, closing in on the city from afar, step by step, ending our trek on the strange vista of Three Rock, looking down over the heaving, poisoned reef of Dublin. There's perspective in that. It's arguably a harder route, with steeper climbs, but I know I have the stamina for it. You just put one foot in front of the other.

My confidence by this point has shakily returned with the administration of my vaccine, received a month or so earlier than CB's. Still, we think the Wicklow Way will be deserted. We think, sure we'll see nobody and one of us vaccinated is well enough for now. It'll just be us skimming in and out of bed and breakfasts and then wandering through the green with our backpacks. Safe.

The sky is very clear and the sun thrums down, and we drink water from enormous bottles. We picnic on a soft patch of grass near the roadside, and the fruit in our little lunch-bags has turned hot. I spritz our faces with a little aerosol bottle of spring water I bought in the pharmacy. In the forest, we see nobody, though briefly I encounter a large rabbit and we are occasionally harassed by large clusters of fat black flies. It is green, and thrumming with life up there. The blackberries haven't come in on the brambles yet, but their promise is all over the hedgerows in little pink-white flowers on thorny vines. On the side of one particularly steep hill, my face is scarlet and puffed and I can only take a few steps at a time because of the steepness. As I ascend, slow and clumsy at the will of my lockdown-softened body, I look back over the short distance we've come—the grey mountains in the distance behind us, the long slope of meadows rolling down hillsides, the slim roads at their seams. The trees still in the summer sun but still breathing, still witnessing us as we trudge the hills. We are so proud when we land at our first destination, exhausted but thrilled with ourselves. God, it is good to be in motion, good to be in a state of play, good to feel challenged, but free.

The pub in the village is still closed from the lockdowns, so there's no pint to lift to our day—and that is the only reminder, really, that we have been hiking in the silent forest while there are still risks.

On the second day, CB wakes up ill. During our lives together, I have experienced the divine mercy of his ongoing good health—great health even—but we are just outside of Shillelagh and he is very sick and there is a new strain and he has not yet been called for a vaccine and the symptoms look like the symptoms of Covid because Covid is not a cough anymore, it is other things now.

We are in a Scandinavian log cabin in the garden of a very friendly woman who lives almost exactly in the middle of nowhere. He lies in the starched holiday home bed, tall and quiet and pale in the face. I have no spell for this. There is no sword for the sudden mystery of a sick husband. Only my phone and my steady voice. Outside, the sun beats down.

***

A regular complaint that players make about *Breath of the Wild* is about the weather. Hyrule has had weather—and times of the day—for a long time, though in previous iterations of this world the snow, the sun, the falling night and heavy rain were merely decorative. Textures layered onto environments for narrative reasons, for a sense of drama, of place. Sometimes Link would find the ice underfoot slippery, sometimes he would leave footprints behind him in the white fluff of snow. Environmental hazards were largely unhazardous to the player—rain could be summoned, for example, in *The Ocarina of Time*, by playing a song and summoning it down, somehow connecting the Link of that story to the elements.

However, the weather in *Breath* is constant, changeable, and interacts with the body of the player almost constantly. Should you find yourself attempting to cross snowy plains, Link will shiver and shake and take damage and, if you are not equipped to warm him, die on his knees in the snow. If you find yourself in the desert, moving towards the city populated entirely by women who live in the heat and the sand, you will find yourself slowed, sweating, staggering, unable to move forward, even if you take off all your armour. You have to protect yourself against the invisible atmospheres of the space you are traversing, as well as lizards the size of men who spring up from the ground, or lurching goblins armed with blazing clubs.

When it rains, you feel it the most. The rain lasts for, sometimes, seven minutes of 'in game' time in a row, and should you be climbing the side of a mountain, you simply must stop where you are and wait for the storm to pass. No matter how experienced, how powerful you are. No matter that you have defeated divine beast after divine beast, that you are a hero sent to save the world. You will stand on the side of the cliff and feel the water rush over you and you can not go on until it is done. The elements do not care that you are on a journey. You are a body, and the world is the world.

***

It is here I need to tell you that a woman called Teresa drove us from Shillelagh back to Dublin, all three of us wearing two masks over our faces. It took a little over an hour, all four windows of her car wide open. I think of how abjectly fucked we were, and how she did not have to help us, but she did.

I also need to tell you that when we got back to the flat, the mountains staring down at us through our bedroom window, CB did not have a temperature and I have never felt more relief in my life—until, the next day, he received a negative Covid test. I texted Teresa. I texted my parents. I texted the woman whose cabin we had been staying in. They were kind, and relieved for us—and likely for themselves, also. That we had not wrought danger on their homes, not brought a hungry and invisible guest with us, on our breath.

Most importantly, I need to tell you that the symptoms for heat exhaustion are almost exactly the same as the symptoms that social media had been telling me all week were sure signs of the new Delta strain. Persistent headache, persistent nausea, confusion, fatigue. We had, in that cabin, no way of telling whether or not the sun had undone CB or whether it was something more sinister.

This was, largely, two frightening days, not some grand arc of a tragedy. The sun had been silently eroding us as we moved, placing CB in a danger that neither of us could protect ourselves from: you can stay hydrated, you can eat well, but a body is a body, and the world is the world.

***

Most weeks now, I manage a couple of very long walks. Fellow walkers do not dip onto the road to avoid my sphere of breath, they do not wear masks outside, no longer am I enemy, am I threat, no longer are they same to me.

I trek the long, straight road from my suburban village to the county line, the invisible marker at Scalp between Dublin and Wicklow. I watch the grey of new houses speckle out and surrender to lush green fields, mountains rising both close to me and far in the distance.

In the late summer by the Scalp Woods, there is a field full of sunflowers and every week I watch them grow taller and taller. It is beside a forest that I will not go into alone, so instead I befriend the volunteers at the nursery, promise I am not a thief, and walk in amongst the sunflowers. I take photos of them, and the sky above me is the kind of grey that promises a drench and it comes down on me as I leave the golden field and I stand under the bough of a tree until the worst of it is over, thankful for the green rubber of my jacket, but still feeling the chill. The sunflowers drink the water and when the worst of it passes I begin to walk again.

As I move back towards the little estate at the foot of the mountain I see, everywhere, things and places I cannot touch. The boundaries of my world are immutable, and I cannot walk to the end of it. There is no line in the sky for me to place my hand upon—the limit is my body, not the hills. The ache in my thighs and calves is something, though. The emptiness there in my head. It is almost good, and in that, it is almost enough.

Talk To Bridget

Lorie Broumand

It turned out the man was tidy and smooth, with shiny sleeves rolled to his elbows and a precise collar. I immediately detected something of him in him, something of his voice in his face, his octagon jaw full of accusation. Fearing he would detect a parallel familiarity in me (*that poor so-and-so's foolish posture reminds me of the foolish posture evident in the voice of Bridget—*), I turned my back to him, and with him the five dozen customers lined up at the front counter. An intricate pattern of stanchions funneled the customers through to my employees, six of them, hunched over their registers with weary fingers, and the front doors—three sets in a row—stood open. Helene, the employee whose register he'd ended up at, had been overdue her lunch break for 20 minutes. She often walks off under these conditions, her caustic head bobbing with insolence, but today she'd held out and ended up with the man.

I realised I wouldn't hear what they were saying with my back turned, so I turned again, risking him looking up and seeing in my posture the conversation we'd had—

But he didn't notice me. He was speaking to her with the same unendurable calm tainting his pronunciation, a sort of accent.

'It's something more than temperature,' he said.

The light was coming in just so, so perhaps he couldn't help but say it, and the absence in the temperature (which I'd tried to identify when we spoke) was very apparent. But Helene didn't have a moment to spare, as her tilting and weaving made clear.

He observed this and said, 'I'm looking for Bridget.'

'She's at Movies,' said Helene, brushing him off metaphorically with her voice but then going one better and actually waving her hand at him with a sideways, scooping motion. This is exactly the sort of thing I tell my employees not to say and not to do. They talk to each other about my overcaution, my lack of ability to let a transaction evolve as it was meant to: as a reflection of those involved, with their own difficulties at the front. *Why should we not be difficult?* they ask me in my head. *We are difficult! This serving of customers is difficult! And the customers, they are difficult! How can you imagine the sum of all this difficulty will be anything but difficulty? Such a thing is mathematically impossible!* But it's never kosher to scoop a customer, I say in response, in my head. That's a fundamental truth, a law of the universe, a mathematic of its own—and a basic one at that! So don't talk to me about math! And Helene, you are the worst! Always scooping customers, always shoving them left and right with the gleam in your eye, always hissing and fizzing over the slightest infraction, like someone saying 'good morning'—

But I'm frightened of not firing Helene and frightened of firing her, and the two are at an impasse.

She was wearing one of her dresses with the big collars. I had a flash of memory about brightly coloured boxes, or cars in the shape of boxes. I couldn't see the movie theatre from my position in the middle of the room—it was tucked down a skinny arm of hallway to my right—but I could smell its movie smell. It's something to do not just with the popcorn machine but with the cleaning solution used on the big glass windows of the projection room and those giant rolls of film. Opposite the theatre was the featured exhibit with its opposite smell: flowers, soil, a blinding green tree with heavy leaves. Behind me were the planetarium, the regular exhibits, the staircases, and the cafeteria; above was the mezzanine all in glass; above that were more exhibits, another cafeteria, escalators, elevators. Tension pulsed in my right arm.

'But do you know the Bridget I mean?' he was saying.

'She's over there. Can I help you?' The 'can I help you' was for the person behind; Helene craned over the shiny-sleeved man as if he'd already disappeared, and she confronted that hapless next person with such hate; oh, the hate she packed into those words! Hate for the shiny-sleeved man, for those behind, and for me—

I could sense her scooping the hate at me with the backs of the heels of her shoes!

He looked at her patiently, and I saw in his jaw that he was not to be dismissed. He was that sort of person—always in it with the right actions to make things work for himself. Or maybe he was just lucky, moving through the worst of life with a lack of displeasure and a confidence in the order of the things in his head. I could sense him sensing that the cells in his brain were all lined up.

'If you'll pardon me,' he said. He was about to take care of business.

But I've hurried past the worst thing: he'd said, 'Do you know the Bridget I mean?' In this terrible phrase I detected it: that he hadn't believed me when I'd said I was Bridget. I knew he knew that no such Bridget existed.

Had he been fully right in this, the situation would have been well under my control. But a Bridget did exist, and she was, at that moment, eating a sandwich over at the movie window. I could see this when I peered past the stucco mammoth that stood along the northern wall of that skinny hallway. I wasn't surprised; those movie people eat sandwiches on even the busiest days. An unruly crowd had formed at the theatre itself, but the movie window was protected as always by the complicated geography of the main front area; customers persisted in coming to us, not them, for tickets. Bridget was telling a story to Tej, the sandwich flopping backward and forward in her animated hand.

Bridget's very nice, but of course that's got nothing to do with it. I'd never set out to orchestrate another's downfall. The problem was the name; surely one doesn't hesitate over one's own name? I'd always had one ready that didn't belong to anyone on the ticket counters, and if the customer came in to ask, it was simple: No, there's no one by that name here. Must have been a mistake. Could you have dialed the number for __ ? Might the sonic sense of __ have dissolved, unwillingly, into __ ? Could it be your ears, I hate to say? Are they mal-attuned to the ticketing timbre? Etc. It still ended uncomfortably, but at least I wasn't dragging someone else into my discomfort, someone who could call out the whole thing; and at least I'd be left to watch quietly from the sidelines, my turmoil giving way to a cautious gratification in the face of my preserved anonymity.

In this case I might just as easily have said Bertram, Batman, or Balloon, and I congratulated myself on what seemed the better option. Then I realised my mistake.

'Bridget?' he'd said. 'Is that what you said? Bridget?'

I'd remembered to mumble, even in my unhappiness. That's what I mean about him: he couldn't let a person get away with a mumble. I could hear it in the way he said, 'et'.

'Bridge. Et—?'

'Yes. Et.'

'Say again?'

If I were a different sort of person, I might have come up with something on the spot—Margaret, for example—and corrected him. Et? Why yes, Margaret. No, not Brid. Mar. Mar*gar*. But— 'There's a commotion behind me,' I'd said in my fear, and I hung up.

His call had come minutes after a new bundle of tickets had accordioned across the floor under my supposedly careful hand. Smith shook her head at me as she walked by. She'd insisted on walking by at just that moment to see it. It wasn't a shake of, *Oh those tickets!*, but more, *Again with the tickets?*, and I was crushed.

But the problem was the light, or the temperature, or something related I couldn't put my finger on: a tone, a smell, or a density. Something amiss and playing incorrectly, a vibrant undertone, or overtone, of summer, when it wasn't yet spring. The tired yearning came over me, a sickness, a sadness. I wanted something that didn't exist and remembered something I'd never known. It had to do with the wovenness of the air, pretending to be something it wasn't.

But one might argue there was no justification for my fighting with him.

'I need tickets,' he'd said with his voice.

We discussed the tickets. He wanted combos that included everything—there was a movie about dolphins and a movie about mountains; there was the planetarium, the featured exhibit, the regular exhibits, the water tours and the sky tours and the light shows—and the planning on his part and the waiting on mine were terrible. I could describe it, but it's not an interesting vehicle for the passing of time.

Then I said, 'It's your day. You've won double the tickets.'

He said, 'What does that mean?'

I'd expected him to restate what I'd said, giving me the opportunity to assure him that whatever he'd thought he'd heard, he'd heard wrong. I could have still done this—*What does that mean is right!*, I'd say—but the whole thing threw me off so badly, you see. And I was facing the big east-facing window, and cars wove into our lot in dense lines, and behind was the quadrant of bridges.

So I said, 'It's a timesing procedure. The number of tickets you need times two.'

'Tickets. You mean for later? Vouchers?'

'No, tickets for today.'

'Wait a minute. I need a total of five combo tickets for today. You're saying I can get ten and use the other five later?'

'No, use them today. You need to use them today.'

'But I need five for today.'

'You can only use tickets today.'

'Can I get a discount instead of the extra tickets?'

'No, just tickets I'm afraid.'

'Just tickets?'

'Just double the tickets.'

'OK, so I'll go ahead and get three tickets.'

'You want three tickets.'

'Then the three more, for a total of six.'

I was starting to feel queasy. I started to want to just give him the tickets as vouchers, for later. But that wasn't what I'd said, and Smith had already talked to me about giving stuff away. She thought it was my generosity to blame and was inclined (or had been, in the beginning; the beginning is way in the past) to overlook it. But the problem now, as always, was I just disliked the man so much.

'It's a one-time thing,' I began. Then I paused for a very long time.

'I'm sorry?'

'You already said five tickets,' I said.

'I want three,' he said.

'Then you can have your three,' I said. 'But no more.'

'Plus the other three,' he said, 'as part of the deal.'

'There's a summer sense even though it's early in the year. That's what I'm trying to get at. Is it something in the clouds more than the temperature? Or is it in the light?'

'You told me there's a deal on,' he said, with infinite, insufferable patience. 'Double the tickets. How do I take advantage of that?'

A miserable cold shuttled through me, reminding me of the wrong I'd done.

'You think you've got your cells all lined up,' I said.

'Synapses come and go,' he said.

Those winding cars were delivering customers, and three of my employees were looking over at me, waiting for me to get off the phone to fix an emergency.

I started to speak again, but just then he started to speak again, and so I stopped, out of politeness, and what he was saying sounded like, 'Speaking's a sign of sadness.'

'What was that alliterative thing you just said?' I said.

'We're all with frantic feet and faces,' I said.

But he only asked me my name, and then we went through all that, and then I said what I've already said I said, and then I hung up.

Sometimes I look out the window at night, in summer, and see figures bending and shifting with lights on their heads. They are workers, doing their summer work, building roads, fixing holes. 'It's cold,' I called out last night, thinking they'd gotten confused, or that a tyrannical boss was insisting they work despite the season. I considered what I might offer to make their lives better. They're busy, or not terribly social, I thought, and that's why they don't speak. 'The light over there is misleading,' I called, 'as it's actually early February, and exceedingly late at night.' They're busy, I thought, which is why they don't respond to my question with even a turn of the head.

He persisted in interacting with Helene, and I could see in her face how wretched this made her. I could see it even though she had her back to me. Yes, I thought, he's a problem. But what do you want me to do?

'If you'll pardon me,' he said, amid the waving of her hands, 'can you confirm there's a Bridget? And will you point her out to me?'

If you'll tell me where Bridget is, I thought.

If you'll tell me—?

A person named—?

He's not so bad, I thought, him and his fancy brain.

Him and his fancy sleeves. Him with the jaw. Sleevejaw. Sleeve-man. Jawfan.

I wanted to encapsulate his nature in a word, but who among us can dive whole into a single word? Who among us can divide, parts equal and complete? None of us, that's who. I felt what I always do at this realisation, a tired old sickness, a sadness. I want to dive whole into a word, me, Bridget Balloon, and the idea of bits of me spilling over the side—well, it's horrifying, is what. And if not me, then the man: if he's spilling over, that's awful too. Might be, might as well be. Might as well be me.

Maybe what I'm saying is, if he can't fit in a word, none of us can. I saw that this was true—I saw it so clearly it was like I was seeing a colony of worms marching through the multicolored sand spilled at the front desk, something from a child who'd tracked it down from the playroom upstairs. It made me feel lost and soggy in a way I couldn't place. Sogman, I thought. I could feel him, or perhaps myself, yes, himself, as Sogman. I felt it deep in my bones, but somewhere else I knew it was just a game. I can't encapsulate my nature into a word, not at all. I am not Sogman, and he is not Sogman; there is no one named Sogman, and no one named Sogman knows anything about me. And yet that same Sogman is quite like me. Fighting the same sorts of problems, like sogcells, like cells in disarray. Cells in dismay. And that made me feel much worse.

This whole time a summer sense was coming in the big windows, despite the cold, and despite the earliness of the year. The lines had gotten longer, as it was now afternoon, the day finally waking up, etc.

'She's over *there.*'

Helene was looking around, trying to find the utensils she might use to be rid of him. Jayla, to her left, or Gordon, to her right, might take him over. She might enlist them with a stare, a half-closed eye. She even looked over her shoulder to me, of all things. But Jayla and Gordon and I were all doing our best, which was quite hard enough without Helene and this man interfering.

I calmly put away bundles of blank tickets with my head up, my ears alert. I heard him say, 'But there's a line over there. Can you walk me to the front of it? Can you call Bridget and have her come over?'

Old shiny-sleeved Sogman, I thought, and for a moment I grieved for him very much. Not for what he was, but for what he wasn't—something complete, with its own comfortable eternity.

Helene and the man, I thought, addressing them. *You're not one worse than the other.*

Don't get me wrong, I was very frightened. But I had no choice; somehow she would get this man and Bridget together, and Bridget would be the Bridget of herself, which is very different from the Bridget of me, and he would detect this instantly—perhaps even before she began to speak, perhaps merely by the merry way she holds her head. She would offer him a bite of sandwich. She would offer everyone bites—

And he would already know from my voice that I would not offer anyone—

And I considered simply walking off the job and crossing that quadrant of bridges. But I didn't have anything with me, not nearly enough clothes for a long journey by foot.

So I intercepted him—what else could I do?—and Helene's relief was apparent in her furious face, and she put up her 'Next Window' sign and left. How I intercepted him was, I said, 'You needn't see Bridget, I can help.'

'Are you Bridget?' he said. Which just goes to show what he'd got his mind made up to, because I'd just said I wasn't.

'No,' I said. I spoke in a funny voice so he'd think I wasn't Bridget. My funny voice. I can keep it up for a good twenty minutes if I have to.

'Where is she?'

'She's gone,' I said, and he looked doubtful.

'Do you know about the Double the Tickets deal?' he said.

'Today? Oh, well, today you can get vouchers for later. Just buy whatever tickets you want and you get the same number in vouchers for later.' It was the quickest way out, and I didn't feel good about it. I knew Smith would somehow find out, and we'd have another long talk about it, and she'd say it was my generosity to blame, and she'd file some unpleasant paperwork even so.

Then old Sogman, he said, 'I wanted to talk to Bridget. I had something to tell her that I thought might help her.'

'Does she need help?' I said.

He seemed reluctant to answer.

'You could tell me and I'll tell her for you,' I said.

But I was handing him the tickets, we were at the back of the counter where the light from outside was coming in and changing to more of a yellow, and he just took them and thanked me. He thanked me and shook his head.

I said, 'But I want to hear what old Sogman has to say.' The name came again into my mind, unbidden: Sogman! Sogfan. But it didn't tell me anything about anything I wanted to know, and I regretted having said it, and I jabbed at my left thumb with my right.

'If you were Bridget,' he said.

'If I were Bridget,' I said.

He made his way out of the chaos of the front desk, and then I couldn't see him anymore.

Well, that's over, I thought, and the mess of the day faded into the bigger mess of the bigger problem. Him just like me, me just like the others, them with their frantic feet.

Anatomy Scan

Let's begin with a shroud, darkened by time,
pushed aside to show the filigree of your bones.
The ultrasound probes and digs as you slither
in and out of focus, sockets gaping
like a Halloween ghost through a sheet.
The hole of your stomach. The chomp
of your heartbeat hungering below my gut.
Perfect cerebellum. A very nice spine.
There—the kidneys. Little dark pockets of need.
Colour flares across the screen, arterial flow
through widening chambers, its rush exhausting.
The eyeball's orbit. Closed but watchful.
Your twig arms flinch and flick. Your tiny jaws grin.
Little lizard. You know something I've forgotten.

Jessica Traynor

The Baby
Jacinta Mulders

Sometimes the Baby sleeps. This is no time for complacency. We use its naps to clean the walls, re-stock the muslin cloths, wash the soiled nappies. If the walls are clean, we clean them again: the Baby's health could be at risk. There is no end to how clean we can make its environment. We draw a vacuum over the big soft armchair. We disinfect the large rattle. We have to stop often because the Baby has woken, is crying for food, needs to be cradled, has shit itself. Every job is related to meeting the Baby's needs, whether it be neurological stimulation exercises or coring apples for pureed fruit.

We try to teach the Baby things, but it is unable to learn. It has an irritated temperament and kicks at the squashy picture books we give it. It knows no words and has not progressed in learning any, even though we have been here for some time now and even though we have asked Camille, who is the most charming of all of us and has the most soothing voice, to tell the Baby a story about a chimp that made friends with a bird. The Baby didn't care. It wriggled and cried so loudly that her words were drowned out. Huge watery tears rolled down its cheeks. In the tea room, we whisper between ourselves, spinning theories about why the Baby is so angry, so recalcitrant and so mean. Camille says the Baby cries because it can't articulate itself. To Camille, the cries are cries of frustration. Melodie, who has a compressed median nerve from rubbing the Baby's back too much, thinks the Baby has a bad karmic load from a previous life. Gustav is ruthless; he thinks the Baby is one in a bad line. According to Gustav, the Baby is the product of bad breeding. Bitterness runs in its blood.

Members of the Baby's family are people of high influence. Consequently, they are at greater liberty to speak freely and behave as they want, as opposed to most other people, who, in this region, must behave as if protection of the Baby—obsession with the Baby—is the highest purpose possible. I can see the utility of working for the Baby. For example, if I didn't work for the Baby, I wouldn't have income. But other aspects of life with the Baby feel dishonest and forced. Like, for example, the idea that serving the Baby and the Baby structuring social and political life is, as an organisational strategy, much richer and more effective than how things work anywhere else.

Sometimes I have conversations with Camille about what people in other regions do. What do they eat for breakfast? How do they spend their afternoon hours? When I imagine places outside of our city, I think about white flowers and narrow lakes. I don't know where these images come from. Maybe my mother, in stories. Maybe I heard them in passing, on the street, or I could have read about them somewhere. But, if I did, I don't remember where.

Someone at work has noticed how quietly and selflessly I have acted, how diligently I have gone about my day and scrubbed stains from the Baby's clothes, and he offers me a special contract. The contract means I can get away for a little while. The instructions are very specific. He tells me to catch a train to a city four hours west. In that city, there is one of the Baby's aunts. She has a life full of freedom and frivolity. In that city, she has been saying mean and untrue things about the Baby. She has been saying that the Baby is only a baby, and that what the Baby needs is a good smack. The task I am given is to convince this aunt, using subterfuge, to return to our city, where she will no doubt be reprimanded or locked up or something. I'm not really on board with using violence, but I don't want to pass up the opportunity to travel four hours west.

I know that if I complete this task successfully, I could get a promotion. Honestly, it's not an unattractive carrot. I'm sick of the room I rent. The way it goes is you spend the majority of your income either on a room or on food. If you spend your money on food, you have to sleep in a hall at work. Because I pick the other arrangement, I pretty much live on tinned chickpeas. Apart from hummus, you can't do much with chickpeas. I've tried it all: chickpea cake, chickpea soup, chickpeas with milk. The others can keep their chanterelle mushrooms, their bushels of green apples, their merlot. All they do in the Sleeping Hall is get drunk and steal blankets from one another.

Other people have been sent out on special contracts. When Paul came back, he was lifted out of Primary Care and into Administration. Apparently he started smelling of vodka after that—acrid and hot—and bought a blazer with sky-blue lining that he cared for, meticulously. Amelia was sent out a year ago. We never openly speculate where she went, but I do, privately, in my head. She might have used the contract as an opportunity to run away. I imagine her hitching rides on alpine trains. I imagine her eating hunks of bread and cheese. She might be sleeping under pine trees, curled up under a blanket made from fine wool.

I enjoy the train ride out of town. My carriage is empty, and there is sharp coffee in polystyrene cups. I expected that life outside the Baby's region would be populous: that there would be noise and people, and that the countryside and fields would be golden and buzzing. But outside, the snow is total. It has a muffling effect, and from behind the window of the train the landscape is white and uniform: fields look like houses, which look like trees. There are no animals that I can see. I try to quash the deep feeling of unease that this landscape gives me. It's a feeling that, actually, life is more uniform than I thought. That maybe people in other regions don't have it better. That their lives are equally full of struggle. Here, the snow banks them in, foiling their plans, snuffing their voices.

In the new city, it is a great luxury to have so much space between the Baby and me. I would like to put off finding the aunt, and walk for days without direction. It gives me a delirious, dreamy feeling. If I am not careful, I will forget myself and my task.

I start at cinemas. She's not in the first one, but I stay and watch a little of the movie anyway. On the screen, people are flying through a forest of bamboo.

The aunt is loitering in the doorway of the second cinema I visit. I recognise her for her grey ringlets, her exuberant clothing. Her frame is slight and aged. Her skirt is the colour of a Vitamin C tablet, and she is wearing velvet burgundy slippers. I follow her inside, where, in the corner of the foyer, there is a lady selling ice cream cones with round chocolate shells, and something smells like butter.

We sit in the theatre, side by side, and watch a film, a film that doesn't make sense. First there is a woman with blonde curls around her face. Before her, there's a mirror with old-fashioned lightbulbs. The woman's mouth forms a sudden O—in ecstasy or in horror. A creature, dripping goop, emerges from a lake. Next, a pilot wearing goggles in an airplane careens over tiny fields. The fields are jewel green. The shot begins to flicker in and out of focus. It looks as though the pilot is going through a series of clouds. The screen goes violet. There is a low droning sound. From the seat beside me, the aunt begins whispering into my ear. Her breath smells like peppermint, and she whispers all the usual stuff, the stuff I was warned about, the stuff I have to be resilient against: the Baby is a foil for faceless power; it is delicious to run naked down the side of a mountain; there is power in choosing your own outfits, like, for example, hot pink or tulle. The words she uses and the way she puts them together are beautiful, musical. They give me chills. The woman with blonde curls and the creature and the pilot begin to make associative sense. I see the possibility of sea monsters living near cities living near pilots living near actresses living near lakes. Sense can be drawn from the conflation, if my mind can slow down enough to draw it out.

I look beside me and see that the aunt is gone. Clumps of chocolate shell from her ice cream are melting on her seat. I could try to find her again, but it's useless. I won't be able to convince her anything I'm saying is true. I am not strong enough to manhandle her ideas or her body; the things she says are too aberrant and too powerful. Listening to her, I would get hot and cold with shame and longing. I imagine myself as an older woman like her. How thrilling to have grey hair and roam the streets muttering. How thrilling to eat ice cream messily. How thrilling to live in this disgusting city and still behave like life is joyous, worth living.

I know it won't be long before they send the guards. The guards could be wearing black shirts or the guards could be wearing white shirts. The guards could be in stripes, or dressed like supermarket clerks. Back in my city, outside the doors of the Baby's building, there are a group of guards carrying machine guns. I have never heard those machine guns go off, but, when I used to pass them, I would see small circular tips where the bullets come out. It might be exciting to hear the sound of those guns break out now. But I doubt, when the guards come for me, that it will be anything so monumental. When I realise what's happening, it will probably have already happened. I wish the aunt would come back and help me. I wish to see white flowers and narrow lakes. I wish for some type of deliverance. I want to live long enough to be a fugitive, for my hair to turn a brilliant and silvery grey.

All I Want's My Goose Back

… geese they don't consider it lawful to eat; they rear them for pleasure and amusement
—Caesar, Commentaries on the Gallic War (58–49 BC)

… poets, like bees, have a very strong sense of property; and both are of that irritable
kind, as to be extremely jealous of any one who robs them of their hoarded sweets
—William Drennan, Fugitive Pieces (1815)

That's the thing about us from here: we're always rotting for the undergod.
I know a fella—barman in Piccadilly—binned a framed photo of Churchill
willy-nilly one Monday night his manager wasn't in

and got away with it scot-free. If it's only for a laugh, who cares?
But I want my fucking goose back.
As an expendable character in the comedy of your life, I wonder why I

annoy myself about your feelings. If I do call the hotline
to the Royal Vocabulary Constabulary,
I'll tell them to quash the charge and that, well, I'm truly flattered. Still,
I want my goose back, or you owe me a tenner.

Something's rotten down on Denmark Street. A beastly camera crew
slouches towards Boundary Way.
In chess they say, Play the board not the player! I want the goose
you stole *I stole* from Macauley, but you can't give me that *Anser anser*.

Scott McKendry

Freak Aguacero
Jessica Gaitán Johannesson

'I have no creative use for guilt, yours or my own.
Guilt is only another way of avoiding informed action.'
Audre Lorde

I

This is how I learned about the climate in Colombia: starting out with a plain template (didn't our country look like a bloated starfish, perhaps one in stilettos?), we were instructed to populate a series of maps, which would later be bound and graded by our primary school teacher. Each map began as the same contour, until the contour itself could be traced almost without looking, and each would serve as a face the motherland wore, a distinct way in which it was la nuestra—ours—as the advert for the Colombiana soft drink kept insisting that it was. Ours in what way, exactly? This was in 1996, in Bogotá, the city where my mother was born.

In January 2019, just under ten months after my mother died, my sister and I go to Bogotá together. We go together, for the first time as adults, but we've been adults for a good while already. Is this why everything feels so late in the day, so much past its use-by date? The Christmas crib is still in our grandmother's fireplace, replete with miniature holy men and sheep, a left-over from the latest major event we missed.

The whole of the first week is spent in our grandmother's flat, occasionally taking her out for sun on the courtyard and, once, taking ourselves to a bakery across the street. When we want to go out for groceries, our aunt, our older uncle's wife, asks if we won't wait until one of them can take us. We have two uncles on our mother's side, and the younger has insisted on staying with a cousin, so that we can have his room. He's left us an impossibly thick duvet, hand-made by a former girlfriend. Either we are being looked after because we don't know how to do it ourselves here, or here, this is how people look after each other, and I can't remember, exactly. Although we used to come here at least once a year throughout our childhoods, and although my sister was born here, we only actually lived here for three years in the 90s. Our mother wanted us to know this as a home, to have this place sewn into us. The celador who guards the block where my grandmother lives says 'hasta luego niñas' ('niñas' sounding so much younger than 'girls') every time we leave the block of flats. We are both in our thirties.

This is how the climate in Colombia was taught to me: by proxy. I was never great at planning homework, and the night before the map assignment was due, my mother and I sat up late. We watered the country with rivers: 'El azul de la bandera es por los rios, niños' (the blue of the flag is for the rivers, kids). We planted vast areas of rain forest. I say 'we', but mostly I stood next to my mother, who sat hunched over the desk, a side-view from on high of her working right hand, drawing what was supposed to be tiny cattle. At the end of it we had a folder—you could flick through it quickly and see the nation unfurl into separate layers of skin, various threads and tendrils. There's no way anyone would have believed this was done by a child. The maps, in any case, would later be sabotaged by a three-year-old, the son of a family acquaintance, who snuck into the room my sister and I shared, in search of who knows what, and doodled all over them.

On the first Sunday of our visit, my mother's younger brother, who travelled around the country with my parents in the early 80s and introduced me to Celtic music when I was fourteen, takes us for a walk through La Candelaria, the colonial centre of town. It's a touristy place, but also a heart of a kind; not knowing it leaves us heartless. The day begins with the usual smog lid on, the school buses exhaling like exasperated whales at every corner. My ears recognise this sound as the prelude to car-sickness—mine and that of other uniformed schoolchildren in one of the world's most congested cities. This is only good; in the business of recognition, nausea does the job exceedingly well.

My uncle parks the car close to the Hotel Tequendama and we walk uphill to see the view from near the planetarium. When in a certain mood, the sun in Bogotá chomps down on your scalp and takes bites out of the thin skin under your eyes. 'El sol aquí tambien quema,' our mother used to say: the sun burns here too. No one thinks of sunbathing in Bogotá. The sun wants you to know that you're edging in on its territory. Other than that, nothing about the explosion that is this city, all okra and uneven roof tops, makes it tangible that it sits 2, 640 m above sea level, a colossal basin filled with almost ten million people and still growing. It's able to breathe but not feed itself. The capital's dependency on neighbouring regions makes food scarcity one of its main vulnerabilities in the face of climate collapse.

On the long flight here, I paid for onboard wifi for the first time ever so that I could look up Spanish terms related to global heating. Cambio climatico, industria ganadera, puntos de inflexion; I didn't have words for the end of my world, in the language in which it began. With a handful of terms, I then try to explain to my uncle, repeatedly over the course of two weeks, why I've gone vegan. 'It makes sense, all those cows and the methane,' he says, jokingly. Cows, I think, my tongue going numb as I try to make the jump from that to 'urgent system change', to the 3 am desperation that makes me want to block roads back home, even though I'm not a UK citizen and could have that home revoked. What do I want him to say? That he will be going vegan too, at the age of fifty-nine, in a country where vegan food remains expensive? Or that he'll be joining a protest to demand action on climate change? What is this 'system' that I want to change—the one which allowed me to grow up on two continents, or the one in which five people from three generations share a smallish flat? Both are part of the same system, that which gave me my life. I'm the result of my father, who worked for a Swedish company, moving to Colombia for a few years and meeting my mother there. Regardless of how much my mother's family is mine, that history, the imbalance of it, puts me on the other side of a global divide.

After spending an hour at the Botero museum, we walk down Calle 11, toward Plaza de Bolivar. The sun has given way to a dusty pressure over the eyes. This is only one of hundreds of squares in Colombia named after Simon Bolivar, el Libertador, but the only one where the assassin of Jorge Eliezer Gaitán—a progressive politician and leader of the Liberal Party—was dragged by an angry mob in 1948, sparking the period known as la Violencia (as if by giving this name to a period of time, violence might have been confined to it). While he was still alive, our grandfather suggested that we were related to Gaitán, but when I mention it now to our uncles, they laugh. There are too many Gaitáns in Colombia for this to be worth pursuing. All of which sounds like an excuse not to dig into things, one I swallow whole. Received belonging can be alienating, but also comfortable.

One of the maps was dedicated to mountains: three ranges born out of one, as if a giant hand at the border with Ecuador filters the Andes between its fingers: la cordillera occidental, la cordillera central, la cordillera oriental. At the very top, there's la Sierra Nevada de Santa Marta, which I thought looked like a spot on someone's forehead, snow at its peak. The 30,000 indigenous people living there, the guerrilla and paramilitary groups fighting over the mountain for decades, weren't part of the map. Our version of the ranges ended up looking more like slug trails, or the veins on the back of my grandfather's hand. Luckily, I didn't tell this to my mother, who must have been exhausted. The maps had been my responsibility, not hers.

The main attraction on Plaza de Bolivar seems to be pair of llamas wearing pink ribbons. One of them is being encouraged to dance. At some point between a quick look inside the cathedral and us finishing our corn on the cob, it begins to rain. Precisely because it comes out of nowhere, there's nothing strange about this rain. Rain in Bogotá often behaves like this, pouncing on your day like a raiding party. My sister, my uncle and I run to wait out the aguacero underneath the awning of a discount shop on Carrera 7, alongside at least twenty others, but soon decide that it's too crowded and start walking toward the car. That word, aguacero, always puzzled me: it sounded like agua-cero, zero water, but refers to the opposite: a ferocious downpour. Aguaceros never remain aguaceros for long, which is what makes them aguaceros, as opposed to any other kind of rain, anywhere else in the world.

Where Carrera 7 meets Calle 19, my uncle cuts a corner a few feet in front of me and is punched in the chest by a vicious wind. It throws me backward and makes him hold on tight to his jacket. My sister's face stretches out to its edges, giving her a stranger's grin. She was born with an ever-so-light line down her nose, a birthmark which our mother said was from the factory where they put the dolls together, and now this line risks being cracked open. In Edinburgh, or Göteborg, a wind like this would be native. It would know its way around the city and understand its routines. Here, its shriek is incompatible with any other sound. We've been plucked up and deposited somewhere else, where winds such as these exist, and where downpours include such winds. The wind, being not of here, has made the weather itself alien— it's even changed the aguacero, derailing it to the sides.

And this is it. I look around to see if anyone else gets it, that this wind is a sign of collapse. You freak, I think, I know what you are, and I am weirdly comforted by the confirmation.

Next, there was a map of major cities. Colombia's capital is located smack in the middle of the Cordillera oriental, in a valley called la Sabana de Bogotá. This places the city in the category of tierra fría—cold earth—as opposed to the tierra caliente of the coast and of lower altitudes. You wear different clothes to tierra fría and to tierra caliente, but neither of them have anything to do with a deadly hot earth. Aged ten, the word 'savannah' only made me think of *The Lion King*, which was also something that happened in the mid-to-late-90s, along with the expansion of guerrilla territory, increased paramilitary atrocities, and Plan Colombia, the local version of the US war on drugs.

II

Upon returning from our trip, my sister and I speak to our family in Colombia once a week. We take turns in calling our grandmother, me to read her stories from a collection by Isabel Allende that we started when I was there (the raunchier—the more wooing there is—the better), and my sister to play traditional ballenatos (heavy on the accordion) over the phone. While my mother was alive, we spoke to our Colombian family almost exclusively through her. She isn't here now to keep the connections alive. It's on us to make sure they don't snap.

On the phone, when my aunt asks what my partner and I are up to, I tell her that we're busy, with 'work and climate things'. I never go into too much detail. It's not that I don't want to tell her, but my willingness to explain, and to be questioned, doesn't stretch far enough.

The river map turned out quite well, I seem to remember—one blue thread connected to another, nerves made terrestrial. 'Los rios de Colombia son muy importantes para el comercio' (Colombia's rivers are very important for commerce), a teacher said, but I only remember stepping into one actual river. It was during a visit to my mother's aunt and uncle's finca in Los Llanos, where it was so hot that we couldn't sleep and our mother sat up waving wet rags in our faces. There was a story about the son of a caretaker who almost got eaten by a snake on the banks of that river, and I imagined the size of such a snake when paddling into it. I didn't think about the relationship between my family and the caretaker, the river and the land. I drew some of the river-map myself, but I don't know the name of that river, or how it's doing now.

There are openings in the months that follow, chances to talk about the climate crisis with my family. My older uncle texts me to say that what my partner and I are doing—the protests, the meetings—is good. 'Either we change or we all go extinct,' he writes, and him using that word, *extinct*, makes me twitch. It's like he's used a secret code, meaning that he knows my fear, and that my fear is real; it exists beyond the particular climate of climate activism around me. Somehow, I must still be thinking that if certain people, people I trust, don't take it seriously, it must not be that bad. My younger uncle texts me to say that I left behind a climate protest flyer on his bedside table (I was using it as a bookmark); does he assume I left it there on purpose? I don't ask. He says it looks interesting and that he'll have a closer look.

I begin to research the impact of climate collapse on Colombia, and on Bogotá specifically. Perhaps I think that, knowing about local floods and areas prone to desertification, I will have a leg to stand on when talking to my family about climate collapse. Really, they've never asked me about my legs, except when I've hurt them. They've never questioned what I'm doing, yet I seem to feel the need to defend myself. I learn that Colombia, being a country where the vast majority of the population lives either in the Andean region (with risks of water shortage and landslides) or along the coasts (where the water is rising), is described by the UN as 'especially vulnerable to climate change'. The country's infrastructure and 'precarious settlements' are part of what make it 'especially vulnerable', especially in relation to other countries, and especially for displaced and poor populations within the country itself. As for Bogotá, there's the risk of dengue-carrying mosquitos making themselves comfortable as temperatures rise, not to speak of the food shortage.

Most of this is accessible climate science, the kind that even I—a 'book person'—have come to deliver in lecture halls as part of this 'doing something', my personal response. It isn't really what I'm looking for. I spend hours searching for mentions of storms in January 2019: a particular wind that didn't behave the way it was supposed to, and that must have been a sign, but none of the results are satisfying. None of them confirm my experience of an aguacero that no longer felt like one.

In April, three months after our visit to Bogotá, my partner is arrested in London for refusing to leave a protest site. On the train home after his release, my younger uncle happens to text to ask how we're doing. I tell him what's happened because I'm still high on adrenaline, and, probably, a little proud. 'Are you sure this hasn't gone too far?' my uncle replies. 'Lo cortés no quita lo valiente,' he writes (the polite doesn't take away the bold), and I reply that this isn't about being bold, but about what's necessary.

Although of course it has to do with boldness, why else would I feel pride? Although a brown person, I was surrounded by mostly middle-class white people during the protest, and this brings with it a certain, more restrained, overall police response—a safety which cannot be taken for granted in Bogotá. Where does this leave my politeness, or my pride? It's a different climate here, I add, to reassure him that as far as the protests go, I'm not in any immediate danger.

We had to memorise the names of each region. Most of them were only familiar from the televised Miss Colombia beauty pageant. I knew that my grandmother was born in Santander, and I recognised the department of Huila because my parents had pictures from San Agustin, a pre-columbine archaeological park. That's full of guerrillas now, my mother said, which meant it wasn't a place we could go then, in the mid-90s. What these guerrilla soldiers did, or why they did it, wasn't part of the formal education about the climate in Colombia. My sister and I knew of the region of Guajira as the setting of the telenovela named after it, but were oblivious to the open-cast coal mine, which, along with droughts, would come to make life untenable for the indigenous people living there.

I ask my aunt over text: what kind of changes has she noticed in the climate over the last, say, five or ten years? She tells me about the birds. Some have disappeared from Bogotá, whilst others, which you never saw at this altitude before, have started frequenting the city. What about the weather? I ask. The wind, specifically, and the rain? I send the same request to both my uncles and instead of a reply, my younger uncle calls me. We talk about his love of hot weather and my uneasiness with it. His dream is to build himself a house with a small pool close to one of the villages about three hours down the mountain. Isn't he worried about it getting too hot? His answer is neither a yes nor a no. He talks about designing a cool enough house (he's an architect by trade), with a wall around it. 'Donde me dejen tranquilo,' he says: where I can be left at peace. Someone can throw food at him over the wall, he says. This would be his life, and it would be fine, as long as no one bothered him.

Talking to my family about climate collapse, I realise that it's not that they don't agree with me on how bad it is, but that they—like me—don't know how to respond. A response to future threats always depends on historical and present dangers, and living your whole life in a country with over fifty years of civil war makes mundane tranquility—simply to be left in peace—a priority. It's not just geography that separates us, but time, a generational shift. Because of all of the above, I've had peace, which afforded me the space to worry about the future. This seems obvious, but when it's your own family, how do you best care?

I mention the aguacero with the strange wind. Oh no, my uncle says, you get that kind of wind every year in Bogotá, around that time. It's because it's surrounded by mountains. 'Eso aquí es así,' he says, which is what he's always said about the insecurity, about not being able to trust people, about always calling taxis instead of grabbing one off the streets, and about government corruption. When he talks about people taking the piss as soon as you turn your back to them, he says 'eso aquí es así'—that's the way things are here— as if he's given up. What's more, I don't know enough about the way things are here to be able to tell him it's not too late. It sounds vaguely like when people say 'it is what it is', which my partner dislikes so much he's made me promise never to say it.

Possibly, this is what I wanted: for someone to tell me: 'You were right.' Which would mean: 'You know this place. You know it well enough to see it change.'

If someone we didn't know asked us for our names, my mother said, we should always give our Colombian surname. The worry was that if they heard our father's Swedish surname, we'd be at risk of kidnapping. 'They' were the guerrillas, but it could also be someone spiking your drink, then leaving you in a ditch (this happened to a colleague of my father's). One day at school, we were all ushered to a classroom and shown a documentary about the drug trade. It presented us with a clinically sparse room and a dead body in the middle, opened like a tamale, being emptied of packs of cocaine. I remember asking the teacher if I could leave, knowing I'd have nightmares, and the teacher said I couldn't, because this was important. I could hold my hands over my eyes, if I wanted, but I had to stay in the room, she explained. That way, at least in theory, I would have learned about what was going on.

III

When I've stood in front of a group of people talking about three, five degrees of warming, or stared at a camera during a protest, willing it to see what terrifies me, I know that, inevitably, I'm speaking from a distance. It's a gap similar to the one between me and the maps, me and the drug-trade documentary. Privilege filters climate fear; inequality makes it a warning rather than an experience, theory as opposed to a lived reality. This doesn't make anyone's fear less real, but it does make a difference, and that difference carries through into our reactions to a crisis which is global, but which is always felt locally, and in endlessly different ways. Writer Sarah Jacquette Ray has asked if so called 'climate anxiety' is really just 'code for white people wishing to hold onto their way of life or get "back to normal"'. Class and economic vulnerability, as well as race, not only determine when, and how brutally, someone feels the effects of climate collapse. That 'normal' was always different to begin with; it never had the same everyday violence and volatile days built into it. This is why, although a global crisis, climate collapse can never be the same crisis globally. When we talk about our most existential fears across class, generational or geographic differences, we're expressing very different vulnerabilities, and different abilities to respond.

It wasn't a lack of vocabulary keeping me from speaking to my family in Bogotá; it was guilt. When I think of the Colombian part of my childhood, I feel guilt because of its privileges—the private, bilingual school it happened inside, the Swedish passport that framed it, and the shelter from harm—but there's also a guilt because of everything I missed when I didn't live there: a war, a peace process, whatever comes after. Finally, there is guilt because now I'm here and they are there, and because I don't know enough about their life to say what's best for all of us, even when this thing, this horror-show, will affect us all.

The map representing Colombia's climatic zones looked like someone had splashed five kinds of oil paint on the country's chubby frame, then smeared them with a finger. Mine, my mother's finger. It was difficult to get to grips with. I stared and stared at it for a long time, trying to imagine what it felt like to live your life in each, to be me in each of those places.

A popular way of explaining the difference between weather and climate is through the allegory of personalities. If weather is a mood, then climate is a personality, it is said. This makes me think of the years when we lived in Colombia, and my father suffered from chronic stress and road rage. Anyone who met him, for the first time, coming out of another 6 pm traffic jam, would have made certain assumptions about him as a person. We knew he wasn't like that, not normally, because we'd known him all our lives. When I ask my family about the weather, I say: 'que tale el tiempo?' which makes the word for weather—tiempo—the same as the word for time. Rather than confusing things further, this may work as a reminder; that in order to truly understand its climate, you need to give a place your time.

In late April 2021, protests broke out all over Colombia. They'd started in 2019, but were interrupted by the pandemic. They are connected to the government's handling of the COVID-19 outbreak, but also to the broken promises woven into the 2016 peace accord (a watershed event I watched from afar, without really understanding its workings), and to so much of what went before—at least half a decade of armed conflict. Between April and early June, sixty-eight deaths were documented by Human Rights Watch, many of them at the hands of the ESMAD, the police's anti-riot squad. If I'd lived there, would I have been part of the protests? If I'd been me, but there, would I have developed entirely different ways to respond?

Instead of asking my family about what's happening, I've been trying to make contact with Colombians in the UK. It's somewhat counter-intuitive, not only because I always resisted connections that are solely based on shared origin or nationality, but because I'm embarrassed to admit I don't know anyone, outside of my family, who is Colombian. In response to the government repression, groups of Colombians in the UK came together in solidarity with the protesters, lobbying the government and raising awareness about disappeared activists. Speaking to one of them, I ask her about her own conversations with family back home. 'It does usually end with that,' she says. 'You know, the *you're not here, you don't know what it's like.*' But she did live there until her early twenties, which suggests that it's the leaving that cuts us off, more than the time spent away. Meanwhile, in connecting with others who worry about their country from afar, and feel responsible for it, she says she's found a place from which to act, and that it's a huge relief.

We don't know what it's like to be there, but the distance also creates a longing and an active, wilful belonging, one which may have its own part to play in a global crisis defined by inequality, in which those most affected, and least responsible, are also the least heard. My connection to Colombia is a narrow stretch, liable to flooding. Especially because it's so late in the day now, it's up to me to feed it, and by learning as much as I can, widen it.

NMS

17th January 2021

Downstream, daytime on the hospital side, running dogs and old women,
Messages in gaps and outlines of before, on stone and tar,
Cracked walls held in hope in steel bracings, endings in mounds of rubble,
And boys kicking balls against parked cars and walls.
A couple, long-skirt straddling in the door of the corporation housing
In the early summer evening, rock gently as you pass
The white plastic supermarket bag, the polystyrene box tumble
Turning around twilight, in the welfare centre carpark.
On main street cheap shops and bakeries announce poverties,
On hand-written signs misspellings: *milk 'n' clothings tok'ns taken.*
The off-licence offers cheap sherries and silver tins
To those waiting in alleys with the perspicacity of herons.
At the abandoned church cats preen behind locked railings,
Languidly regarding their offspring tumbling in bundles
On litter so thick you can no longer see what lies underneath.

Gary Boyd

Golem

Wendy Erskine

It actually takes the taxi only ten minutes to get there from the hotel. Kind of erotic, that driveway, with its crunch of gravel and soft curve. As Marty pays the driver, Rhonda watches two women walking past in sorbet summer dresses. When they get out of the car, Marty and Rhonda follow the women who are heading in the direction of the music, the soft and happy chatter.

Look at them! Rhonda says. You should've put something better on you than jeans and a T-shirt!

Doubt it matters, Marty replies. Hardly think I'm gonna be centre stage, Rhonda. Hardly think I'm gonna be the star of the show.

They pass between the side of the big house and the wall covered by creepers and azaleas, hydrangea and clematis to get to the garden. That is where the marquee is, its awning flapping just a little in the breeze. At the entrance, on a white table, there's a wicker basket for presents. Rhonda deposits the photo of the young Eloise and her. It's wrapped up in silver paper, so no one sees the two of them as kids, perched on the bonnet of a car, wearing deely boppers.

The garden was empty and the marquee only half-erected when Eloise first looked out this morning. Edgar was there already with the hose and the noise-reduction headphones. He bought them to use when cutting the lawn, but now he wears them for tasks involving only slight sound.

Don't you miss the birdsong, Eds? she asked.

Not really, he said.

Of course he missed it. He was striking a pose, just as he did when he listened to that plinkety-plonk music with the geometrical shapes on the front.

But Edgar had done the lot today: the caterers, the marquee, the invitations. He'd booked the flight home for Mimi and he had asked Martin and Rhonda to come over. Mimi's hair was black now and it suited her, Eloise thought. She'd seen a photo. They could go for a lunch, the two of them. When the caterer's van arrived, Eloise noticed the name in calligraphic script on the side. It might be nice, winter sunlight, a velvet sofa, to sit and do calligraphy for an indeterminate time. Was it considered art? Probably not. Oh well. Then the hairdresser arrived. She asked Eloise if she wanted it sleek, like last time. Sleek was like an otter, a thing arching its gleaming body by a riverbank. Or maybe a stoat.

No, I think don't let's go with sleek. What else is there?

Voluminous.

Then let's have that as our goal then. Voluminous.

A little volume was more forgiving anyway. She liked to make an effort. If she read a book, Eloise always looked first at the picture of the person on the back. If it was a woman who didn't look like she was making the effort, she knew she wouldn't enjoy the contents. (Of course some tried the reverse, tried to tone down good looks with functional clothing or a crude haircut, but they weren't fooling anyone.) But those other sorts, with their sad frizzy hair and watery eyes, they would consider her stupid. And they would be right. Not so long ago she met a woman who told her how, after doing a couple of exams at the local college, she was studying for a part-time degree. It all seemed very straightforward. The woman had ended up finding out lots to do with medieval people. In fact, they became a passion. She was very taken with something called the Carolingian Renaissance. It wasn't so difficult to imagine herself also being interested in the Carolingian Renaissance, or in fact another renaissance. It needn't be that one, particularly. When she told Eds that she wanted to do a course at the college, he bought her a very good pen as a present. But when she went, the man at the front spent aeons talking about the features of classic liberalism. It was all quite impenetrable. Eloise decided to shift to Art, where she made a clay model of a frog, filled a notebook with charcoal drawings and made a time-lapse film of raspberries rotting. The teacher came round one day and said that she needed to figure out what she wanted to say and what was important to her. The teacher lifted the photo of a drainpipe that Eloise had taken.

Is this important to you? she asked.

Not really. It's just a drainpipe.

But I want you to consider what's important to you. She added gently, What would that be?

I don't know, Eloise said. All sorts of things.

Like what?

I don't know.

It was only when she was driving home that she realised what her answer should have been. Mimi. Mimi, my daughter is important. Mimi. Mimi.

On the way to the airport, Marty had been saying that he still couldn't understand why they were staying in a hotel.

Because, Marty, Rhonda said, did Eloise and Edgar stay with us when they came over to Belfast? No, they didn't, and so staying with them on this trip was just never going to be on the cards.

But when they came over, we never asked them to stay with us.

Well of course we didn't! Where would they have slept? Could you imagine those two on an inflatable mattress on the living room floor? Hardly think so.

Okay, so even though they asked us to stay—because let's face it they have fucking rooms galore—we have to say no, because they didn't stay with us, even though we never asked them to.

Yeah you got it, she said.

Even though it is going to cost us the guts of three hundred quid.

Yeah you got it.

Money well spent then.

Rhonda affected a serenity. Know what, Marty, it's actually not going to cost us anything. Because it's costing me. I am paying for the hotel with my money. And because I am paying for the hotel with my money, why don't you just shoosh?

There was silence until they got to the short-stay car park. Taking the bags from the boot, Marty said, I would have to point out, Rhonda, in all fairness, that it's not really your money anyway. It's Noreen's.

Was Noreen's. A solicitor, flakes round her mouth from eating a croissant or other pastry, had told her just how much she and Eloise had inherited when their mother died. It wasn't much.

My money now though, Marty. My money now.

As they progressed through security, Rhonda dreamed of Edgar. Her mother, incontinent, dazed, aching, had even so refused to go into a home. Put me there and you will kill me, she said. Is that what you want to do? So before and after work in the hospital, Rhonda tended to her. At the end of a shift, when they were as usual short-staffed, Rhonda just wanted to flop rather than start work anew at her mother's. The home-helps were useless. Don't expect me to light a fire! one of them said. All I can do is switch things on or off! Eloise sent care packages of hand-creams and candles with complex scents. One time she posted some chilled desserts.

Rhonda got to Noreen's one evening, found her lying covered in blood. She'd fallen and hit her cheek on the grate. It needed ten stitches through paper-thin skin. Rhonda phoned Eloise to tell her. Even though it was Edgar who answered, she provided full detail on how long they had had to wait at the hospital, how it was bound to happen again, how it was all practically impossible, how it was unfair that everything was left to her to do, how enough was enough was enough was enough.

But Rhonda, he interrupted to say, Eloise and I can help. In fact, Eloise and I should help. We should be doing more.

He said he would give her a phone call the next day and he did, just as she was loading sodden sheets into the washing machine. He'd had a chat with Eloise and if Rhonda thought it best that her mother should have full-time care in her own home, then they could certainly fund it. He would leave the exact arrangements up to her but he wanted to give her his bank details. And so she started thinking about Edgar, a man who had only ever represented polite conversation, fucking her. It began when she woke at six o'clock in the morning, thinking that she needed to get to her mother's freezing house. She had to light the fire and get her up out of bed, washed and dressed. Then she remembered. No. No. The carer would already be there. The duvet seemed softer, warmer, and the world was a more benevolent place. It wasn't money though. Rhonda despised all that stuff where women went drippy over billionaires, submitting themselves to some guy's every whim because he had the dirty cash. Gimme a shout when there's a film about a woman throwing it all away for a guy on the minimum wage! Rhonda would say. She phoned Edgar to express her thanks. He listened so carefully to all she had to say that she found herself telling him about her day at work. So it wasn't just the money. It was understanding and, in fact, know what, understanding was actually really, really hot.

While the little overhead vent on the plane had been blowing air in her face, Rhonda had been lying on a beach somewhere with Edgar. He had just brought her a drink in a tall glass. He rearranged the beach umbrella, and the little breeze stopped. She reached up and twisted the black plastic. It was endlessly sunny with Edgar and sometimes they lived in a house she had seen in an interiors magazine that belonged to a professor at Stanford; a house in Palo Alto, all greenness and beautiful wood. So warm there too. There was always golden late afternoon light when they had sex.

Sorry, Marty said. I shouldn't have mentioned to you about your mum and the money.

It's alright, she said. Forget it. At the end of the day, you're right. It's her money.

At the party in the garden, Marty and Rhonda still stand at the entrance to the marquee. There is a string quartet in evening dress on the left and there are a couple of young women in white shirts and black trousers, carrying trays of drinks in long-stemmed glasses. There is a smell of cut grass. Everyone knows each other: their easy laughter confirms it. Marty and Rhonda feel a little awkward. Then Edgar appears. Wonderful to see you! he says. Terrific that you could come! He gives Rhonda a little kiss on the cheek. Marty! he says. Guess what? I got beers. Rhonda smiles at Edgar, then looks away. But then she looks back at him again. A woman comes over to say that someone needs a word with Edgar. I'll be right back, he says. Eloise is just over there! She'll be thrilled to see you!

The air-steward's cheery voice thanked them for travelling with the airline.

What time are we getting back tomorrow? Marty asked. You know I have to be in work super early to let those plasterers in?

After the debacle in the previous job, he was keen to make no mistakes in the new one. He had allowed the boy Dino out to pick up one of the team from the garage where his car was in being serviced. That wasn't permitted, but still Dino was behaving well, he wasn't a bad lad. But Dino had picked up a girl he knew, crashed into a car, and put an old woman in hospital. Before doing that he and the girl had stopped off somewhere to have a burger. It was all in the papers. Young Offender Burger and Smash Bender. Marty had to resign.

Getting back at a reasonable time, she said.

You looking forward to seeing Eloise?

*

The last time either of them had seen Eloise was the day of Noreen's funeral. They all went for a meal in the hotel where they were staying. The restaurant was so like an opium den, it was a relief to get into the bright white of the toilets, refreshing to see the arc of yellow against the white. He stood there longer than he needed to, until someone else came in. Edgar ordered wine from the menu the waiter gave to him. When the bottles of white and red were brought to the table, Marty asked for a beer. Afterwards, Rhonda said how rude it was. You could have passed yourself, Marty. I mean, there was red and there was white.

Neither of which was what I wanted to drink, because that was a beer.

That wasn't it at all. You were acting the big man. Don't think you are all that, pal, that's what you were saying. I'm not having your wine. I'm having a beer.

Okay, let me tell you this a minute. You seem to operate in a world where everything seems to mean something else entirely. It's all code. I ordered a beer because I am an adult guy and I felt like having a fucking beer.

Yeah yeah, I believe you. Keep on telling them.

But she had got it wrong. He had no problem with Edgar, the radiator king. His family had made a fortune through central heating and good luck to them. Edgar, as that type of guy went, was fine. He enquired about Marty's work, asked what made it difficult. He remembered about the BMX riding.

Isn't that usually for little children? Eloise asked.

Yeah well, that's actually a pretty common misconception, Marty said.

I've never really seen adults do it. But I'm sure little children would enjoy it.

Eloise, said Rhonda. Marty was in quite a big competition over in England. If you had been at that, you would have seen plenty of adults because it was an adult competition. He can do all sorts of moves and tricks. They require a lot of control.

Did you win a trophy, Martin? she asked.

Yes, he said.

Well done.

No, it was Eloise that he didn't like and never had. Bottom line: she thought she was better than Rhonda. Any time Rhonda spoke she looked bored. And then, when she spoke, it was something entirely unrelated to what Rhonda had just said. She was self-centred. Postnatal depression, fair enough, no joke, but why did they have to hear of it endlessly when Rhonda couldn't get pregnant at all?

At Noreen's funeral, the two of them stood side by side, like one of those 'before' and 'after' shots, Rhonda being the two stone heavier 'before'. So what he did was, he beckoned Eloise over. He's standing near one of those droopy crematorium trees. She comes over, unbuttoning her black dress as she does so. Sometimes he fucks her over the tombstone (Sorry, Noreen!) and other times it's over the bonnet of a car because the car park for the relatives and other mourners is only yards away. She keeps begging him to hurry up, but he just takes his time. Takes his time. Nice and slow. Harder, harder, she says. But he keeps his own pace. She turns round. Do it on my face, Marty, she begs. I might, love. Or know what, I might not. Let's just see how it goes.

When he finishes—without doing it on her face—he walks back to where they're all standing, forlorn and in black. He goes over to Rhonda, gives her a hug and a kiss. Eloise looks over, furious, and he smiles slowly, happily.

Let's go over, Rhonda says. There she is. There's Eloise.

She is standing with a group, who are laughing at what is being said by a man with a booming voice. Eloise is poised and beautiful in a lemon dress.

Happy Birthday! Rhonda says as she gives her sister a kiss.

Yeah, many happy returns, Marty says. He gives her a hearty pat on the back.

I take it these are relations? says a smiling woman in a long dress with safari detailing.

My sister, Eloise laughs. And this is Martin, my brother in law. When did you arrive?

About five minutes ago, Marty says.

No, I mean, when did you arrive over?

The little string quartet begins a medley of Beatles songs. The viola player nods and smiles, seemingly acknowledging the whimsical nature of this.

The party guests would arrive at seven. Many had been invited but there were only a few that Edgar really cared to see: Marty, obviously, and Mimi. There had been a problem with the marquee but they would adjust the bill accordingly. It was meant to have had a laminate floor and white sofas. It was a glorified beige tent, open along one side. Others had arrived with bundles of lilies in zinc buckets and piles of linen. Eloise, Edgar thought, might not appreciate the beige. They had recently had a room in the house painted white. Surely white was white, but Eloise had got charts of various whites because some, he was informed, were cheap. She knew about colour. A while ago she had painted a picture. He found it a little naïve but it had been chosen for an exhibition in the library. On arrival, they found a dot beside it because someone had bought it, so he feigned mild outrage that it was going to be in someone else's possession.

He was on the way to pick Mimi up from the airport. This he would enjoy doing because he liked driving. It wasn't velocity. He didn't care about going fast. He would happily go on an endless journey, driving in silent darkness on smooth, unspooling motorways. He didn't even especially care for cars per se, even though he got a new one every two years. He always used the same dealership; they sent him invitations for new views and promotional events. He went once. They showed a video of a new sports car on a massive screen and people passed round trays of miniature burgers. But Darren wasn't even there. Edgar looked about the room, the shining chrome, gleaming paint, the crumpled looking individuals. He always got Darren every time he went. Darren was maybe in his thirties. He wasn't a typical car salesman: not slick or loquacious. He had no patter. In fact, he said virtually nothing, but filled out the paperwork with a world-weary air, as though it was sad that this beautiful and expensive new car would change precisely nothing. He didn't call him Edgar or Mr Bryans. He didn't call him anything at all.

Edgar had only ever seen him once outside that place. Eloise had a dreadful headache and they had no tablets so he said he would drive to the shops to get some. He didn't know why but he drove past the garage with its little shelf of painkillers behind the counter, and headed to the supermarket instead. Maybe it was because of the longer drive along an empty road lined by dark trees. He ambled around the shop because he wasn't sure where the tablets were. In front of a chilled cabinet, with his back to him, he saw Darren. He stood there compact and still. He was holding a basket. It looked sad, the basket. Why couldn't he just carry what he needed? Darren put a pizza in the basket which already had a carton of orange and a loaf of bread. Darren looked tired as he moved on, but perhaps everyone looked tired under the white lights of the supermarket. Edgar was there the next week, at the same time. He told Eloise they needed milk. He poured the last two inches of the carton down the sink. But Darren wasn't there, even though Edgar was systematic in his exploration of the aisles.

He wondered how Marty and Eloise's sister were getting to the party. Had he been told to pick them up too? He couldn't remember. He would need to check again with Eloise.

By the time they got off the plane, the shuttle bus to take them to the terminal was already full so Marty and Rhonda had to wait, with a handful of others, for its return. They were last off because Marty had got everyone's luggage down from the overhead lockers. Come on, Marty, wise up, Rhonda said. No need to act like Sir Galahad for every woman on the goddamn flight.

Marty wondered if the party was going to be wall-to-wall with ex-models. Eloise used to be a model. Noreen had loved going on about it, right from the very first night he had ever gone round to the house. So you know Rhonda, but have you met my other daughter, Eloise, the model? she'd said. Marty had once gone out with a girl who did the same sort of stuff, so-called modelling—in other words, handing out crackers with cheese at a milk marketing board event, or handing round plates of chicken drumsticks in a hotel in the town, while wearing shorts and a T-shirt. He mentioned as much to Noreen.

It's called promotions work, Noreen had said. And not everyone can do it. She's also been on the cover of a magazine.

What's it called? he asked.

Never heard of it, he said, when she mentioned the name.

You think any of those model friends of Eloise's will be there? he asked Rhonda, as they headed towards the car-hire desk.

Doubt it. Sure it was years ago. Doubt anyone would've kept in touch.

Funny how you are one of the best-looking people in your town but you head off to the big bad city and you're two a penny. You know, the teen queen hits Hollywood and she's washing dishes.

Well somebody has to get a lucky break.

Didn't happen for your sister.

Well, Rhonda considered. She met Edgar.

Don't know if Edgar is my idea of a lucky break. Right, let's get this car sorted out.

The man said that they could have an upgrade if they wanted, to an E-class Mercedes. It wouldn't be too much extra.

Why bother? Rhonda said. It's hardly any distance to the hotel. And there's no point getting a fancy car just to impress them because we'll be getting a taxi there.

Jeez, it's nothing to do with them. I just want to drive a different car. Yeah, that's what we are going to do mate, he said. Let's go for that E-class.

*

When Mimi appeared in arrivals, Edgar, as he hugged her, managed to kiss her enormous gold headphones rather than her cheek. Wow, he said. Those are impressive. But she explained that actually they weren't and that anyone who knew anything about them would know they were a piece of shit. She launched into a labyrinthine tale about various people borrowing and losing headphones.

He laughed. Okay, then, those are very unimpressive and shit headphones.

Her hair was black but there was an inch of fair at the roots. Her grey tracksuit bottoms were bulky but her skimpy white halter top showed her nipples. As they went towards the exit, he saw people stare at his daughter, at her white top. She wasn't as bad as he had seen her on some occasions, but still her shoulder bones protruded, her chest was knuckled. It was so long ago when it started, fourteen years of age, with that boyfriend who took the dreadful photos of her and sent them round for all to see. The police couldn't do much. But then it could also have been the school. Too much pressure. They sent her to another place. Too little structure. When they went all those times to see that fancy doctor who played Joni Mitchell in the beautiful waiting room, it was always her and him. Not Mum, she said. No way do I want Mum there. The journeys back, both of them faking a brightness that something was getting a little better.

You must be cold, darling, he said, when they walked to the car. Perhaps you should put on a jacket. Do you have one?

She said that she would only be staying for one night before she headed off to see some friends.

I'd love you to stay longer, he said.

Maybe I'll hang around another day. But only to please you, you crazy old fool. Who wants me to wear a coat.

She punched his arm, laughed, gave him a kiss.

Rhonda looks out from where she stands in the marquee to the beautiful big house and its garden. There is a patio area with fat tubs of flowers. The place is just looking so well, Eloise, she says.

Eloise has such a special sense of style, one of the women agrees.

I mean, it's so lovely, but can you remember, Rhonda says, when we used to play in that old back yard? We would do that thing, can you remember, when we were kids, where you put a tennis ball inside a pair of old tights and then you stood with your back to the wall and bounced it from side to side?

Sounds quality, Marty says. Anyone fancy giving it a go now? You got that big wall over there.

Mimi used to have tennis lessons from a young man who went on to be a reality TV star.

And do you remember, Rhonda says, that there was this other thing we did with elastic bands?

I didn't watch it but I heard that he was quite popular.

Don't really know, Marty says. There were a couple of girls who were pro-surfers. And there's always loads of fitness instructors isn't there?

Don't talk to me about fitness instructors! says the woman who thinks Eloise so stylish. She holds up her hand. Just don't talk to me about them!

Rhonda wondered about the party as she stared at the fields out of the window of the car. Hopefully it would just be Edgar and her, for at least some of the time. She wanted to tell him about her life, because he would understand it. So many things didn't compute, but if she told them to Edgar, they might become clear. When she came off the phone to him that time it was as if all had been rinsed in cold water. It's Edgar's house and she's drinking brandy in a beautiful glass, clinking the ice when she pauses in telling Edgar whatever she's telling Edgar. She's watching herself on a big cinema screen, her back arching, her mouth open. A physical manifestation of Edgar never really appears in her mind. He's just more of a presence, but what is annoying is how there's always a radiator in shot. It always sneaks in, the radiator. The only place it didn't appear was the beach.

So Marty didn't think that Eloise had lucked out when she met Edgar. Well, what did he know? Left to her own devices, things hadn't gone too well. Horrible to remember it, but things had not gone too well at all. The other times she came home from London she was desperate to go out with that crowd of hairdressers she knew, but this time she went straight to her room. She was thin anyway; it was like hugging a cat. Rhonda had always seemed to have an extra layer of muscle. This time, when they picked Eloise up at the airport, she was haggard. Back at the house she changed into a geisha-style dressing gown and took to her room. She was in there for the next two days, only emerging to make herself a cup of tea or to have a shower. You okay, pet? Noreen asked every time she appeared. You okay, pet? What's up? Rhonda said. Why don't you tell us what's up?

On the third day, Rhonda went in, opened the curtains and said, We are fed up with you moping about.

She said that she wanted to be left alone, told her to go away.

Rhonda sat down on the bed.

So—what's wrong? You better tell me.

I was—

And she put the arm of geisha satin across her face.

You were what, Eloise?

I got… hurt, she whispered.

Hurt? What do you mean? Who hurt you? What do you mean hurt, you mean you're upset?

She shook her head.

Then what do you mean?

Assaulted. She silently mouthed it.

Oh Eloise, she said.

Sexually assaulted. Again, mouthing the words.

Who by?

She was doing a shoot for a magazine. And after he said to her if she would like to go for a drink. Why not, she thought, but as they made their way down a flight of stairs, he pushed her against a wall, started kissing her, stuck his hand between her legs.

And then what?

He put his fingers inside me.

What a sleaze. What a perv.

Yeah, she sniffed. I know.

I'm so sorry, Eloise. But go on.

Go on what?

What happened next?

Well, there was someone at the bottom of the steps. There was an office below. He heard somebody coming, so he stopped, and I went off.

Lucky escape!

It was horrible. It was disgusting. She pulled the duvet up to her chest.

I'm sorry, Rhonda said.

It was the worst thing that has ever happened to me.

Rhonda said nothing.

The worst thing that has ever happened, Eloise said.

Noreen was shouting, saying that the tea was on the table.

Seriously?

Eloise looked surprised. Seriously!

Well, Rhonda said. It happens. Fellas are pigs. You know, I was only in fourth year when that happened to me. The guy's hand was like an iron bar. And it happened when I had that summer job in the hotel bar.

It hadn't happened to me before, Eloise said.

In a way, you know, I'm surprised about that. If I'm honest. Stuff like that, it's horrible and shouldn't happen, but it does—to plenty of people. And worse. Thing is, that world—modelling, photography, films, telly—it's seedy in its own way. You can dress it up with awards and all that, but some actress is getting paid to pretend to have sex with some grotty wee guy. What did Marilyn Monroe say when she got her first big contract? That's the last cock I'm going to have to suck. That's that world for you. So even though there's all the glitz and glamour you kind of know what you are getting into.

Eloise said nothing.

And so I suppose, Rhonda said, that that means I probably feel more sorry for some seventeen-year-old getting fingered round the back of the supermarket by the deputy manager, you know?

Eloise said nothing.

That's not to say I don't feel what happened to you was bad. But no need to take it personally.

Eloise didn't ever tell Noreen. She packed up her bags and went back to London the next day. And then a few months later, news came that she was now working part-time in an estate agent's. They had used her in their latest brochure; the picture was of her smiling and handing over an improbably large key to a smiling man in a suit. It wasn't Edgar, but Edgar did turn up, some months later, to sell a flat.

So yes, Edgar had come to the rescue. Maybe there would be a crackling open fire at the party, with the wind howling outside. It didn't matter that it was summer. Rhonda crossed and then uncrossed her legs. She just felt so hot.

Those heated seats in the E-Class, huh? Marty said. Pretty good.

Look, there's the sign for the hotel, Rhonda said.

Two people in the group drift off to speak to someone new who has just arrived and is waving over frantically. Another man joins the gang and starts talking to Eloise. He tells Rhonda and Marty that he lives just down the lane.

Is that so? Marty says. Sorry, excuse me a minute. And he heads out of the marquee into the garden where it's less stuffy. He takes a drink from one of the passing trays and sits down on a garden seat near the patio. He sees a girl leaning against a tree, looking at her phone.

Hiya, he says.

She carries on staring at the screen.

Did you hear me? I said hiya.

She looks up and says, Yeah, I heard you.

Not your kind of party?

What do you think?

Come on over here till I have a talk with you, he says.

She makes a pantomime of reluctance, but still she comes over and sits beside him.

I'm Marty, he says. And you're Mimi, yeah?

She gives him a smile of a kind that he has seen many times over the years. From girls, but boys too, fifteen, sixteen, seventeen, trying to be seen as worth something in the only way they know, by being a hot ticket. And she is still doing it at what age, twenty? He looks at her evenly, the way he does with the kids at work.

What do you normally do with yourself? he says.

I don't know. Not much.

Like what?

I don't know. This and that. Why, what do you do that's so significant?

Rhonda sees them talking from where she stands inside the marquee. The circle widens as a few more people join the group. Edgar is one of them. She can't look at him. Instead she looks at the ground. He is wearing little slip ons with the kind of rubberised soles that extend up the back of the shoe. They are for old people. All ideas of Edgar are eviscerated: Palo Alto, the beach, the fire. Vaporised.

Marty and Rhonda saw that the hotel had some half-hearted topiary. An old red dog lolloped down the steps of a shabby white building.

Bit of a dunderin inn, Marty said.

Shut up, it's a four star.

There was a huge white bed with a padded headboard. The bath was a sunken marble affair in the shape of a shell. Rhonda got out the dress she'd brought to wear, and the present for Eloise.

What is it? he asks.

A photo of the two of us when we were younger. It's in a beautiful frame.

I'll put on that other T-shirt in a minute, he said, continuing to lie on the bed.

We're both wearing deely boppers. Remember them. Those glitter balls on wire that you wore on your head?

Yeah. They were stupid.

The dress when she put it on didn't really suit her. It wasn't all about looks, but there was no need for her to wear stuff his granny would have worn. That dress, it was like a dressing gown, tied in the middle. Eloise would take one look at her and think aren't you just so fucking unimpressive.

That the only thing you got with you? he asked.

Why, what's wrong with it?

Just kinda, well nothing really, it's fine. Just wondered if it was the only thing you'd brought.

She undid and did the belt as though that would effect a transformation.

Oh yeah, that's better, he said.

Eloise, he imagines, is wearing those deely boppers and they are bouncing up and down, springing on their wires as he fucks her again. She puts her hand up to rearrange them, but he says, Never mind them. She's over the tombstone. She's over that car bonnet again.

Are you just wearing that T-shirt?

Yeah, why not?

You not making more effort?

Not really, no.

Well, you need to be on your best behaviour with Edgar. I would really appreciate it if you made the effort with him.

Make the effort to do what?

To be friendly.

I am friendly with him.

How long will it take us to get there?

Fifteen minutes tops.

The string quartet is playing a waltz. The girls have brought out square plates of food, decorated with nasturtium flowers. An old lady, another neighbour, is talking about how she used to have a huge number of nasturtiums in her garden. From a distance it looked like the house was on fire. Mimi is bringing a bike out of the garage. It had been there since she was a kid. It's greyed with dust, cobwebs on the handlebars.

Nice antique you got there, Marty says.

He wheels it across the lawn.

But can you still show me how to do a trick?

He rides around in small circles.

What's your balance like? Can you do this?

He stands up, his feet on the pedals.

The old lady is watching, thinking of her husband, long dead, who rode a bike every day to work. She remembers how the bottoms of his trousers sometimes had streaks of oil from the chain.

I probably can't do that, Mimi says.

Try it.

She can keep it poised for a second or two before it skews to the side.

Marty takes it back again.

Okay so, he says, what you need to do is sort your foot placement. You need to get that right.

Again he goes round in small circles, getting comfortable. Marty has been riding bikes since he was a kid, outside shops, in garage forecourts, under motorway flyovers. He lifts the weight of the bike off the ground. He circles, and then does this again, the bike moving off the ground a little more.

Edgar is looking over now, at this sight in his own garden. Marty is in a white T-shirt, his arms creamy and muscled. He thinks of the showroom, the new cars, the supermarket when it is late. Marty lifts the bike so that it hops with the front half off the ground. Edgar smiles sadly.

The bike hops again, first the front and then the back.

It's just not the right type of bike, Marty says to Mimi, laughing.

More people now, drinks in hand, are watching the spectacle.

Mimi, he says, bring over one of those there chairs would you?

She fetches a small white garden chair from the patio. He is able to jump over it. A couple of people clap.

Hey! Mimi says.

Eloise sees it, smiles in delight. Bikes! Now wouldn't that be a lovely thing. She and Mimi could go for a bike ride somewhere. They could hire them and it could be a pretty spot, dappled light, whizzing through a nice forest. But look at Martin and how he just seems to get on so easily with Mimi. How can he do that? How can you do that? Does he know what to say? She imagines going through the forest on her own, slowly.

Come on, give it a go.

Marty gets off the bike and hands it to Mimi. Try even just standing again, he says.

This time she is able to hold it for a few seconds. People, including Rhonda, continue to watch from the marquee. They look like a father and daughter. He would have been a good dad. She would have been a good mother. She thinks so, at least.

Marty takes the bike back again and once more hops over the white garden chair. They all clap once more. A few shout, Well done! And then the string quartet starts playing a sprightly version of Happy Birthday. The bike is left lying on the grass.

Lochán Carraige

lochán carraige
a chart an fharraige
isteach léi i dtonn
is a thréig ann

ina thimpeall an triomach
cloch gaineamh is creag
i bhfad uaidh an taoille
a bheatha

éisc ar an ngannchuid
go gortach tostach
an ceangal acu briste
le scoil is le treabh

a mbéilíní cruinne
ag bogadh mar thaibhsí
gan éisteoir a thuigfeadh
nó a d'fhóirfeadh

a súile gan dúnadh
go feasach ag breathnú
ar chraiceann an uisce
á ísliú

an ghrian anoir
á ndalladh is á dtriomú
an lochán á thachtadh
á ídiú.

Eoin Mc Evoy

Lake Among The Rocks

lake among the rocks
the sea has flung
in there on a wave
and abandoned

stone sand and crag
are parched on every side
and the living tide
is a long way off

a meagre few fish
hungry and wordless
their bond broken
with shoal and with species

round little mouths
parting like ghosts
with no listener
to know or assist

their unblinking eyes
have a keen sense
of the meniscus
falling away

sun glare in the west
is drying up
this lake cutting off
its life.

Seán Lysaght a d'aistrigh

linguistic stripper

(A, B, C, D, E, F, G, H, I, L, M, N, O, P, R, S, T, U)[1]
Mary O'Donnell, 'An Irish Lexicon,' 2013

the/ came across the sea
/ith lassoes for our tongues
more letters than /e had before

      e/er/ speech and drama lesson starts the same
      this
      that
      these
      and those
      for fear of a slip of the tongue
      a dis, dat, dese
      the /ail of a banshee

O/id blamed a disappointing se/ual performance on a /itch

      at uni/ersit/ girls slept /ith ta/i dri/ers for mone/
      proud the/ /ere of being able to pa/ their o/n /a/
      to be independent as orphans
      to be modern /omen

1   The Irish language alphabet has only 18 letters.

i read some/here that cursing
is pre/alent in Irish men
because of their rage towards /omen
to/ards the religion and the language
that suppresses them

       supressing rage
       ensures the alliance of
       m/ speechlessness
       m/ po/erlessness
       the rain in Spain lies mainl/ in the

ho/ long do /ou ha/e to push against something
the fire door in /our mother's apartment
the creases in /our palms
the realms of comprehension
before /ou get tired
la/ /our head against the cool steel
and SUBMIT?

Emer Lyons

Dave's dick-shaped horn cake

he has the face of a fella with a belief in his own destiny
not like us **GIRL**
we'll be fixing that retaining wall for years yet
when it comes to love the fella next door is mad about himself
pops his head in to remind me
tells me he knows what it feels like to be a **WOMAN**
dave shaped his cake like a dick instead of a horn on the bake off
it all goes lopsided once you start weaponising mistakes
I love the cigarette hole in my yellow faux fur jacket
so 90s **KATE MOSS**
it's hard to straight up ask for help **AS GAEILGE**
without making it sound an occasion for apology
unbow your head
water me in your gaze
take a mirror to yourself and make a cake of what you see
would paul hollywood laugh at that?

Emer Lyons

The Interview
Jim Toal

He can't see a thing. Not until it's too late. Braking only sets the car skidding towards a lorry slewed across the road. He knows what will happen. Worse still, as the steering wheel rears up and his head is propelled forward to meet it, there's nothing he can do about it.

A dark surge of anticipation wakes Morgan. Anticipation of impact like lost hope. Of pain deferred, setting his teeth on edge. A throbbing bite into ice.

He pinches his jaw. Rubs the hard slope of bone under his stubbled skin and thinks about the interview tomorrow. But does he want the job after all? He doesn't think so. Not really, though he's tried to convince himself otherwise. Then again, he can't back out now, can he? No. Besides, he's made plans. He's committed. Anyway, a change might do him good.

So later that morning he departs for the market town in rural Devon where he's booked into an Airbnb for the night. Over two hours into his journey, as he's driving over a long stretch of bleak moorland, Kate phones. He puts her on the car's speakerphone.

'Dad? Thank God you're okay.'

'Why's that?' he asks, though he already has a good idea.

'I had a dream.'

'And?'

'You were killed in a car accident.'

'Lovely,' Morgan says, feeling again his face about to hammer into the steering wheel, shattering his front teeth. He hasn't told Kate that he's been having the same dreams as her since his break-up with her mother. While she's ever eager to share her dreams with him, it would be an intimacy bordering on inappropriate for a father to share his dreams with his teenage daughter. A smell of burning infiltrates the air conditioning system. There are red signs by the roadside warning drivers not to leave the road. Access to the moorland is prohibited.

'Well, here I am.' He puts a hand on his chest to feel for his heartbeat. 'Alive and well, I think.'

Smoke funnels from pyres in the distance, clouding the sky. Morgan has seen several while driving over the moors, all of them with vehicles parked nearby, dwarfed by the fires.

'How's things with Bryn these days?' he says.

Bryn is a former colleague and Maggie's new partner. Morgan's and Maggie's divorce went through four months ago.

'Being a complete dick, as usual,' Kate says.

'And Mum?'

'Doing my head in about university.'

As Kate complains about the tuition fees—does she really want to rack up so much debt just for the pleasure of reading a few mouldy books on medieval history?—he pictures her at study. Granular light slanting through a tall library window. The smell of turned pages.

'So, Mum tells me you're moving away?' Kate says.

'Just, you know, keeping my options open.'

The smell intensifies. A file of army lorries thunders past.

'Remember when you singed Cindy's coat?' he says.

'She just stood there like a dope while I got over-exuberant with the hairdryer.' Kate laughs. 'God, I miss that dog.'

'She was a good hound.'

'The best,' Kate says. 'Good luck with the interview, Pops, if it's what you want.'

'Who knows,' he says. 'But thanks anyway.'

He arrives at his Airbnb just after seven. An old-fashioned place with brown wainscoting, floral carpets, and a smell of boiled potatoes.

He hangs his suit up in the bathroom to take out the creases while he showers. Afterwards, he opens the window. Though it won't be sunset for another hour, smoke from the moors occludes the April sun, casting the street into sombre twilight. The shrill alarm of a thrush alerts him to a tabby cat licking itself on a garden wall. A smell of burnt wool and roasting meat loiters in the air. He shuts the window and draws the curtains. Not hungry, he makes do with a cup of tea and two prepacked coffee biscuits found in a drawer. He lies on the bed to read about the school where he has his interview the next day, but soon his eyes tire.

Waking with a jolt, he rereads the same information, only for his eyelids to droop again.

Eventually, he gives up and decides on an early night, returning the papers to his briefcase.

The mattress is hard, the pillows thin and lumpy, and deep into the early hours he's disturbed by rumbling traffic. He gets out of bed and goes to the window. A convoy of pick-up trucks drives past, headed and tailed by military vehicles. The cargo beds of the pick-ups are covered, but every now and then a hoof or a tail pokes from under a tonneau cover. He counts over twenty trucks, each one fully loaded and heading up to the moors. After the convoy passes he goes back to bed, only to be tormented by a nightmare.

In the morning, Kate phones.

'Just rang to wish you good luck, Pops.'

'Thanks, but you already did.'

'Also, I had this terrible dream last night.'

Again, he guesses more or less what's coming.

'What about?'

'There was this big bonfire. Animal carcasses piled up. And you know the most horrible thing?'

Disrupted sleep furs Morgan's tongue. The gruesome image of poor old Cindy scars his thoughts. He scrapes his front two incisors over his tongue and swallows down the bad taste. 'What?'

'Cindy was on top of the pile.'

Kate describes almost everything he dreamt; except, in his dream, Cindy was still alive and yelping as the flames melted her flesh.

'Must've been our talk about the hairdryer.'

'Guess so,' she says. 'It was really upsetting, though. You know?'

'I'm sorry, my love,' he says, rubbing his greasy forehead. 'Listen, thanks for the call, but I've really got to make a move if I'm going to be on time.'

*

He sets out for the interview in good time and parks near the gates to watch the children entering the school. It's a tip he's learned to test the behaviour of the pupils. If they are wild and unruly on entrance, they're sure to be difficult to manage in class. But what does it matter if he doesn't really want the job? Come on. Relax. If it doesn't feel right, just walk away. No big deal. Anyway, the kids seem a pretty placid bunch, only the odd one having a crafty cigarette before the bell and most wearing tidy uniform.

Driving on to the school grounds, he follows a pick-up truck of the type he saw the night before. He gives way while the truck stops to let out a girl who looks about eleven or twelve. A man in green overalls and white wellies gets out the driver side. Pushed back on his head are goggles that have imprinted their shape in his skin, leaving behind a pale band on his dirty face where his tired eyes stare. He gives the girl a peck on the cheek, hops back into the pick-up, then speeds round the one way to the exit gates.

The school is a mixture of Victorian brick, 1960s concrete high rise, and wooden demountables. A serious boy with hair gelled tightly over his scalp shows Morgan to the main entrance, where he steps through a tray of murky, chlorinated liquid that splashes his shoes and soaks into his socks. He straightens his tie, signs in at reception, and takes a seat.

Because the other two candidates have not turned up, the head teacher tells him in her office, things are being rescheduled. They are sat at a long table, the head at one end, swiveling on a black office chair, Morgan at the other.

She has an overshot jaw, and, as they wait for her PA to prepare the new timetable, Morgan is relieved to be distracted from her exposed lower teeth by a knock at the door. A small, thickset man comes in and introduces himself as David Clive, Chair of Governors. A muscular neck strains his shirt collar. With an intense, unsmiling face, he looks on the verge of crisis. Morgan wipes his palms on his suit trousers before shaking hands. David Clive grips his hand for an uncomfortable length of time, squeezing hard.

'I'll be seeing you shortly,' he says, which sounds to Morgan like a threat. With that, he turns away and promptly leaves.

Eventually, the PA brings the new timetable. The boy with the slicked-back hair appears again and leads Morgan down a dim corridor to a small, sparsely furnished office where David Clive is waiting. He flicks a switch and a strip light blinks and hums into life. There's a table in the corner with a chair facing the wall. He asks Morgan to sit on the chair, which he does, staring at the blank wall. On the table between Morgan and the wall is a glass of water and an A4 booklet resembling an examination paper.

'Not yet,' he snaps when Morgan touches the paper. 'You need the instructions, first.'

Attached to each question is a statement. There are five options to respond: Strongly Agree; Agree; Neutral; Disagree; and Strongly Disagree. He sits rigid over each question, each statement. Then he ticks neutral for all of them and puts his pen down.

'Finished, already?' David Clive says.

'Yes, thanks.'

David Clive takes a sharp breath and gets out a mobile phone. 'I'll ring down to reception for you to be collected.'

'What's your name?' Morgan asks the boy with the gelled hair as they walk back down the same corridor. So far, the boy hasn't said a word.

'Karl.'

'And do you like school, Karl? This school, I mean.'

He looks at Morgan as if he's an idiot. 'I have to come, so I come.'

Back in the reception foyer the burning smell has returned but the receptionist who brings Morgan a cup of lukewarm coffee doesn't mention it. He's been asked to teach a lesson on imagery to a mixed-ability Year 8 group. Sipping the cheap chicory coffee, he goes over the lesson plan in his head. Mediocre, he thinks. Maybe he should've prepared more thoroughly, but then again extra hours of agonising probably wouldn't have made much difference. It seems any flair he once had has long since deserted him. He's no better than satisfactory; that damned-by-faint-praise term he's always despised.

The bell rings, and David Clive reappears.

'Follow me,' he says curtly.

In the classroom, the head teacher is pacing between the desks.

'The children will be here any moment,' she says. 'Mr Clive and I will be observing.'

As they take their places at the back of the classroom, Morgan goes to the teacher's desk at the front and opens his briefcase. Soon the corridor fills with oddly muted chatter. The head teacher clears her throat. There are children at the door waiting for permission to enter.

David Clive shuffles paper in the manner of a news presenter and glares.

Morgan dashes to the door to greet the children, who are lined up on each side of the entrance, girls one side, boys the other.

'Good morning, Year 8,' he says. 'My name is Mr Reynolds, and I will be taking your lesson today. If you'd like to come in and take a seat.'

The children file inside, much more subdued and orderly than the kids he's used to teaching. Among them he notices Karl, who showed him around earlier. He sits at the front desk arranging his pens and pencils in a neat line. Two rows behind, gazing out of the window, is the girl dropped off by the pick-up truck at the start of the day.

His throat constricts as he addresses the class. A memory of observing Bryn teach for the first time comes to mind. He was Bryn's mentor during his initial teacher training and responsible for his professional development. While he'd experienced Bryn's confidence mushroom into an overbearing presence, the kids seemed to love him. When, out of a sense of duty, he invited him over for dinner, it hadn't taken long for Maggie to fall for his charisma. The affair had lasted more than a year before he found out.

'Today,' he says. 'Today, we will be learning about the importance of imagery in writing.'

The head teacher begins scribbling notes, and David Clive leans back in his chair.

Although exceptionally well-behaved, the children are passive and impossible to engage. Each question he asks rebounds off a wall of silence. He decides to make things topical.

'Who can suggest an image for what's happening up on the moors?'

The girl, who has continued to gaze through the window, turns her head to face him for the first time. Her chin trembles, and she dabs the corner of an eye with a finger.

'Yes,' he says to her. 'Would you like to contribute?'

At the front, Karl is sharpening his pencils to needle points. The scent of wood shavings enfolds his desk. He holds up his hands and waggles fingers smudged with graphite.

'I need to wash my hands,' he says.

'In a moment, Karl,' Morgan says. 'I'm hoping that…' He looks at the girl by the window. 'I'm sorry, I don't know your name.'

'Jenny,' she says.

'I need to wash my hands,' Karl repeats, more loudly.

'It's not polite to interrupt,' he tells Karl. 'You'll have to wait.'

'Jenny, have you got an image for us?'

Jenny sucks her bottom lip and shakes her head.

'Let me help you,' he says. 'The smoke. How might we describe the smoke? Think of the smell perhaps?'

The head teacher stands up and darts between the desks. David Clive folds his arms. Karl shakes and grinds his teeth, then shouts, 'I need to wash my hands!'

'Mr Reynolds,' the head says, approaching Morgan's desk. Her face is pained, and, as she speaks, a fleck of saliva shoots from her mouth, landing on Morgan's cheek. 'I'm afraid your lesson has taken an unfortunate direction.' She turns to Karl: 'You may go to wash your hands, Karl.'

She returns her attention to Morgan as he wipes his cheek. 'Didn't you read the notes about the children?'

'Yes,' he lies.

'Then you'll be aware of Karl's needs. And I would suggest that you steer the lesson away from what's happening in our community. It's far too upsetting for the children, as you can see.'

Morgan nods an apology, and the head goes back to her seat.

Jenny stares out through the window again, a view of a football pitch, opening onto farmland devoid of animals.

Bryn, he thinks, would get a response. Bryn, who has a natural ability in the classroom, a presence he can only dream of. Bryn would have these kids eating out of the palm of his hand. He'd play them like he played Maggie. He'd soon have them singing, rhapsodising, falling over themselves to please him. He remembers walking through woods with giant ash trees. In the winter huge icicles often bearded the exposed roots and Kate, as a little girl, would point at them gleaming in the pale sun. 'Can you see me? Look, there I am! Inside the ice!' And he'd nod and say, 'Well, would you look at that! Must be her majesty, The Snow Queen.'

The lesson limps on until the bell relieves them all. This time the head's PA turns up to show him back to reception. She gives him another cup of coffee and asks him to wait until the end of morning break.

Many winters later, they took the same path through the woods to the ash trees, where he told Kate about Maggie and Bryn. The icicles, once long and fairytale-bright, were stunted and dismal. Kate picked up a stick and smashed an icicle. 'Fuck Bryn!' She hit another, then another, until she'd broken them all and a spray of jagged points sequined the leaf litter. In the stumps of ice left behind on the tree roots, he saw himself, an attenuated figure, fissured and grey.

The last stage of the process is the formal interview. Morgan is invited back into the head's office and asked to sit in the same seat as earlier. David Clive and the head are positioned at the far side of the table.

The interview is conducted rapidly, and Morgan finds it increasingly difficult to concentrate on the questions as he's confronted by a jumble of discomforting images: Cindy consumed by flames, Kate's face encased in ice, Bryn and Maggie fucking on a bed of diseased carcasses, his face smashed into the steering wheel of his car. He runs his tongue over his front teeth, smooth and delicate.

'We'll be in touch,' David Clive says after the interview has finished. He stands and comes round the table. Morgan isn't sure whether he's going to shake his hand or put him in a headlock. He does neither. He simply opens the door to let him out.

'Safe journey, home,' the head teacher says.

As the PA escorts him to the exit, he hears strained laughter coming from inside the head's office.

He puts his things in the boot of the car and slumps into the driver's seat, feeling drained. Once he's driven out of town and reached the road crossing the moors, he has to pull in. He loosens his tie and turns on the radio which is broadcasting a road traffic alert. A caravan has overturned on the M5, the sprightly announcer says, causing a pile up. Expect long delays. Morgan closes his eyes. The sleepless night has caught up with him. He'll have to take a detour, but it doesn't matter. It's relatively early. Even if he has to take minor roads, he'll still arrive home before dark.

With that thought, he drifts off and dreams of Kate driving, a child—a girl—beside her in the passenger seat, crying, howling, and Kate reaching out a hand of comfort, there, there, only for the child to crumble to ashes under her touch. Immediately ahead, vehicles begin swerving and weaving wildly between lanes. She slams on the brakes and jerks the steering wheel to avoid colliding with a lorry jackknifed across the inside lane. A booming thud. Grinding of metal. The sensation of a soft, warm wetness. A burning smell. Smuts of soot like black rain. Rapping on the glass. A man gestures for him to wind down the window. Ahead, the road is blockaded by army vehicles. Smoke streams over the road, obscuring everything beyond. Looking at Morgan through googles suckered to his face, the man soon becomes shrouded in smoke so that the only thing left visible is his detached head floating in a thick, white fog. While the man hammers on the glass, Morgan reaches for his mobile. He dials Kate's number and waits for her to answer. Pick up, Kate. Please, pick up. Please! The man attempts to open the car door and, with Kate's perky voice telling him to leave a message, the door swings wide open. The cabin floods with the nauseating smell of incinerating flesh, and through the choking smoke a hand grasps him by the scruff of the neck. He knows what will happen next. As his head is wrenched back, he braces himself for the inevitable impact. Face slammed into the steering wheel, his head is dragged back and slammed again. And again, over and over, and with each blow he surrenders further, and deeper, until his teeth crack and shear like snapped icicles.

My Memoir, Scene 7

Yeats, in the Present and the Past, a Sligo Graveside Epiphany

the open sea offers a pledge   to be redeemed upon dying
but when the time comes deny us a distant prospect
his name the guide to one aspect of an encounter with the man
this morning has been twenty years pending   the wail of the wind fiercens
the silent grief of Ben Bulben a tight ghostly blue
a rhyming verse for the whole world   an echo of a rolling wave

a hundred million fossils perforate a bloodstained seam
I hop from ledge to ledge   as if treading on sea spray
my shadow incorporates creatures   that crawl along the shore
miniscule bodies clog my frenzied breathing
bearing light   eyes trapped in crevices
stacked slabs of images whose time is past

what is there left to say   the words of the chapel
incised on the tombstone   the moon shines
repels a Ben Bulben daring the kitchen window
along the ridge a wisp of blue   his poetry
fills my vision   twenty rancid years
surprise me with a worthy vintage

mellow enough now to keep him company   to while away Ireland
emptiness charmed by the stark screech of a gull
he speaks softly   flickering fish scales stitch the open sea
seemingly landing but near to embarking
as the throat of a rusty steam whistle drinks in boggy summer
this kiss   a savour of farewell   lingering on the lips

soaked to the bone as usual   blown dry like a local by an exhilarating gale
his gravestone redolent of the earthy smell of cool luxuriant moss
the panorama ladens my breath with brine
a white cloud emanates from the sea the image of a horseman passing
a covenant   like a ship dead still on the sea's blue hem
our one-off glimpse from a consummate prospect

Yang Lian | translated by Seán Golden

To Believe I am a Carpet Beetle

my grief a warm place for the beetles to home.

behind her books on the windowsill their little legged corpses in polka dot arrangement.

in the school play they cast her as gregor. i trick my way into being mrs samsa.

my grief the pilgrimage from bedhole to blenched window.

wearing the paper maché shell she teeters like an orb waiting to be discovered.

never again the basement room. daytime soaks temperate house. sunbeams worry the plants like toothless weapons.

the difference between infestation and infection is house size. her voice fills my cavities.

they crawl up the windowsill for sex not death but one always follows the other.

to be gregor you must transform your soft nerves into arthritic right angles.

we move towards the light. we hope to find mates before we die.

the beetle small enough to be difficult to carry. i make it a shroud from toilet tissue. it is a caul. it is artificial pupae.

when we love we love the creature. that's why our friend's boyfriends seem so inferior. they hide their pink bellies with duffle coats.

the pest controllers heat the flat to 48 degrees. we throw our candles onto the balcony.

you have too many clothes, they say, before diving in mouth first.

what do you expect when you collect secondhand furs. a plague upon your back.

no past before early 20s. no memory beyond thick mucus skin.

the larvae eat dead materials expunged from living bodies. wool, cotton, silk, taxidermy. dust starved dusky wiggling blind baby.

she thinks with her back hairs.

sometimes i want to be with her, sometimes i want to be her, sometimes i want to squash her.

my grief a quiet place to share a meal.

excuse me, uh, attagenus pellio? please, she says, call me the beetle.

Phoebe Eccles

Aftermath

It had burned. It had rained.
The world was winter,
a worked-out quarry, gouged
dells of shale glimmering
in the blear everywhere

without the least tempering
of clay or vegetation.
Boulders reared up, melded
into corkscrew shapes
extending to every horizon.

I saw clean through
my own body a track beaten
by a vanished machine;
felt no contact when I put
my hand against a sign

of gobbledygook lettering;
sifted amid unresistant
char-dust, revealed only flat
ghost-marks of petals
stunned into limestone.

Shadows spun noiselessly by.
I debated a crow, a root,
a shank of pliable trash
from the time of ambition.
What now was meant?

The ground signalled a lasting
oblivion. Still I walked,
tugged by old anticipations
of finding a homegrown
heaven on earth—the swell

of voices, colour, life— – and yes,
majesty and malady
infuriatingly woven together.
Only ruination stood,
such vast conundrum

mouthing nothing. Why then
this ratcheting of hope,
this search for a future
both faint and foolish
that I had begun to imagine?

Patrick Deeley

The Devil's Rope

Steel 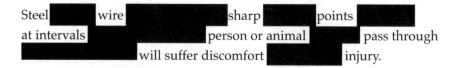 wire ███ sharp ███ points
at intervals ███ person or animal ███ pass through
███ will suffer discomfort ███ injury.

A collector of histories,
of skin and hair
and blocked migrations—
ten thousand cattle dead on a Texan plain,
of shreds of plastic,
of rusted helmets and broken bodies
pinned out on a rack for birds to pick at,
of clothes gripped by fists of metal,
khaki, or something striped
part of a star.

Across the field I see her turn and limp towards me
her dark bay splashed with a gaudy paint box pink
that for a moment takes me to Sunday afternoon art,
small hands and lopsided princesses
but closer, a sliced butchery,
integument breached by the snatch of steel knots,
disclosed flesh weeping.

A history of violent enclosures
in scribbled loops entangling sky.
There are those who walk the land
and those who divide it
and for those who wrap a candle
to light the darkness,
there's always a gap
if you're careful
where to put your hand.

Ilse Pedler

Watching the Detective
Aaron Obedkoff & Patrick Stasny

'My literary project is in direct relationship with my life. My literary project is my life... The literary project, the poet's poem, is the poet himself.'
Roberto Bolaño

THE INTERVIEWERS

Of the many places in which he lived, Roberto Bolaño spent the longest in Blanes, a smallish seaside city about an hour north of Barcelona on the southern tip of the Costa Brava. He moved in 1985 after allegedly discovering the city by chance. Flocked with tourists each summer, Blanes was founded before the Roman Conquest and has nearly been levelled twice since—first by a fire in the eighteenth century and later by a storm in 2008. From his apartment just a few blocks up from the beach, Bolaño helped raise his two children while hurriedly writing the works that would secure his legacy before his death in 2003.

Downtown Blanes has a mix of large buildings from the time of Franco, fashionable takeaway businesses, outdated video rental stores, and small fishermen's houses. This eclectic mixture is typical of Blanes—the name of which comes from the Latin *blanda*, meaning *soft*—a town in which inconsistency seems to be the only consistent feature. Bolaño described Blanes as 'a city which is older than New York and sometimes seems like a rabid mix of Tire, Pompeii, and Brooklyn.'

And so we passed time at a bench in front of the beach, just a few hundred feet from Bolaño's old apartment. In the distance, a rock promontory extended into the water and split the otherwise flat beach into two halves. Here, prompted naturally, we began to discuss Bolaño's story, 'Beach', in which a narrator describes his life as a recovering heroin addict in Blanes. Following his death, this story formed the basis of a rumour that Bolaño himself had a problem with drugs that factored into his early death. In fact, it is all but impossible to parse the mythological from the actual in the story of Bolaño's life. Just as with Arturo Belano and Ulises Lima in *The Savage Detectives*, his life has continued to be a source of conversation amongst a chorus of his friends, enemies, and acquaintances.

Much later, from the bench by the beachside, we called Carla Rippey, one of Bolaño's friends from his youth in Mexico City.

CARLA RIPPEY, on a Zoom call from Mexico City

Well perhaps let me begin by introducing myself. I'm Carla Rippey, but you know that. I was born in the Midwest, in Kansas City, and I left as soon as I could. I went to Paris and then I studied in New York, and that's where I met a Mexican student [Ricardo Pascoe] who went down to Chile to study when Allende was in power. And at that time, I was extremely involved in the feminist movement, but I left it all to go down and get married to Ricardo in Chile—being involved in the Chilean Left seemed even more interesting. But then the coup came, and Ricardo's school was shut down and we had to leave because everyone knew that foreigners were Leftists. So we came to Mexico and I've been here ever since.

In Mexico City, Ricardo was very involved with the Chilean refugees. Somebody, probably Juan Estaban Harrington, took Roberto to meet Ricardo and then they came home to our house. From there we were really quite good friends. But then Roberto's family got into a complicated situation. But as you said, with Roberto everyone has their own version of the story. His sister had an ex-boyfriend who was arrested for holding up a restaurant, I think. So the police got involved with the family and took Roberto down to the immigration headquarters and he took his articles about his poetry and said, 'I'm not a thief! I'm a poet!' Then Roberto's mother and sister went to live in Barcelona and he followed them. I never saw him again. I remember I went to the airport with my kids to see him off. That's where I met his father, in the very first days of January 1977.

We wrote for four or five years until my life got really complicated and it got very hard to answer Roberto back. But then, around '95—like 12 years later—I wrote him a long letter and sent him a package of my shows because I had decided to dedicate myself to being an artist. He said that when he got the package he was afraid it was a manuscript being returned. Then he wrote me a 10-page letter back, the first letter I ever got from him written on a computer. It was a wonderful letter, but I never answered it.

Finally, in the year he died, we started writing again. In May, he called me but I didn't answer, and I tried calling back but I couldn't find his number. When I eventually got in touch with him, he said, 'Carla, Carla, I can't have my number public with all my fans.' We had a really nice long talk. I think, in a certain way, he was saying goodbye.

Then he wrote one last letter to me, I think in June—something about the light on the Mediterranean. Then he died, and I found out from the newspapers. And I remember I was working in a school and I just went around crying all day. It's funny—in one of his letters he writes about meeting me and Ricardo and he says, 'You all gave me so much and I felt like I could never really give anything back.' But he really did—not just to us but to everyone.

THE INTERVIEWERS
The Sailing Club of Blanes is an austere, modern establishment in front of a small marina full of the wealthy locals and tourists who so intrigued Bolaño. He probably never ate here. It's easier to imagine him at a cheap bar in front of the beach, where he could watch the mass of tourists whom he praised as 'Europe's bravest', by which he meant the 'people from here and from the other side of the Pyrenees, the fat, the ugly, the skeletal, the prettiest girls of Barcelona, children of all kinds, the old, the terminally ill, the hung over, the half naked…', an image that reveals both Bolaño's fascination with crowds and his occasional penchant for cruelty.

José Peguero had known Bolaño since the days of the Infrarealist movement in Mexico, where they were young pranksters agitating at the fringes of the mainstream literary circles. Some four decades later, he spoke of these times with a mix of candour and sincere enthusiasm.

JOSÉ PEGUERO, at The Sailing Club of Blanes, Blanes
In *The Savage Detectives*, I appear as Jacinto. I do not recognise myself in the novel except in some parts. And in other places he describes things that

happened to me but he ascribes them to different characters. In the *Detectives* my name is Jacinto. In another, he didn't even bother to change it and my character is named 'Peguero'.

There were several Infrarealists who were angry at Bolaño's portrayal of them, but the ones who were really angry were those from the 'official culture'. So much so that until very recently he was not mentioned in Mexico, and up to this day the Infrarealists are excluded from the history of Mexican literature. Us characters are wondering if one day we should all get together and tell the story as we saw it. Remake the *Detectives* with the real witnesses...

CARLA RIPPEY, on a Zoom call from Mexico City
He did other portraits of women in that book which were rather terrible but mine came across well. My role (Catalina O'Hara) was very small, but there were parts of it which were true, like when I was going around crying because I was having trouble with men. Actually, I had written to Roberto about my breakup with Ricardo.

He really was a myth-maker, and he was himself part of his myth. But he was not a narcissist. He was much more involved with everybody else than he was with himself. That's why he was such a good writer because he had enough empathy that he could write about female characters as if he was them.

THE INTERVIEWERS
We met Bruno Montané at Bar Cèntric, a small tavern in the centre of Barcelona—the same bar where his character, Felipe Müller, offers his testimony in *The Savage Detectives*. Like Bolaño, Montané was born in Chile, lived in Mexico City, and was involved with the Infrarealists before moving to Spain. After settling in Barcelona in 1976, he became the publisher of Editorial Sin Fin, where he still prints, among others, the works of fellow Infrarealists. Like Bolaño, he is also a poet.

Bar Cèntric was dominated by noise, people who had just left work and the regular customers already sitting down, ordering beers and carajillos—a short coffee with rum or cognac. From time to time, a walker stopped in front of a nearby signpost, small and darkened, that read: 'The writer and poet Roberto Bolaño Ávalos lived in this house (Santiago de Chile 1953 – Barcelona 2003.)'

BRUNO MONTANÉ, Bar Cèntric, Carrer de les Ramelleres, Barcelona

I found it funny that he put me in his book, but a lot of things are made up or distorted with endearing genius. You have to smile. At the time there was a very sensitive, somewhat hurt, reading from the Infrarealists which I suppose was unavoidable. The *Detectives* is a novel of a generation, but there is a distortion of the biographical image. I have always said that the *Detectives* is 77 per cent fiction and the rest is biography. Recomposing the theatre of your past is a very curious manoeuvre, but it is always done and has to be done. Roberto managed to build and rebuild a world.

But, as a matter of fact, we did not go so much to Bar Cèntric—which was a bit expensive—but we went to La Granja Parisién, which has since closed. In its place they have set up a phone shop, as they always do.

PIEL DIVINA, in an email from Fontainebleau, France

Another interview about Roberto Bolaño, his work and friends, I thought everything was said a thousand times. The questions are crap and pointless. Perhaps tomorrow I'll feel more inspired. Good night.

PIEL DIVINA, on the phone from Fontainebleau, France

The nickname 'Luscious Skin' was born with the Infra-Realist group. Mara Larossa—Maria Font in the *Detectives*—was caressing my skin one day and she told me I had 'Piel Divina'. Sometimes these things are imposed on you and you just have to accept them.

It is necessary to separate the novel—which is totally fictional—from the real. But it is clear that Roberto could not start from scratch; a real departure point is necessary. The Luscious Skin in the novel is a fiction, and the one in real life is someone else. The person who has dedicated himself to becoming a sculptor is separate from that of the novel. Now I'm doing what Bolaño never did, in a literal sense, being a sculptor. I am grateful that Roberto made me more famous, and it did not create any conflict or sense of schizophrenia in me. It's funny, you know, my character, who seems the most invented, is the only one who does not have a pseudonym, the only real one.

THE INTERVIEWERS

It is a black and white photo of Roberto in a public square. Where? Maybe in Barcelona. He stands on the right side of the frame, staring plainly at Enrique Vila-Matas, who in this instance is the photographer. He is dressed smartly—

yet casually—in a black jacket. His glasses, as usual, take a dominant position on his face. His expression is neither enthused nor unenthused. There is a bag slung over his left shoulder. We must assume it holds books. Behind his left shoulder is a man in a suit, rushing head down with a cellphone pressed against his ear. In motion he blurs such that Roberto, in comparison, seems statuesque.

ENRIQUE VILA MATAS, Crep Nova, Carrer del Comte d'Urgell, Barcelona
Bolaño was not a Beatnik. He was passionate about Kerouac and had read all the Beats. And his demeanour could be like that sometimes, but he was not a professional beatnik in the way he lived his life, nor was he in the past.

The myth about his drug addiction is completely false. It emerged from a commission series called 'The Summer Story,' which was a common thing here, some years ago. So *El Mundo* newspaper commissioned him to write a short story, not an essay. There, he told the story of a drug addict. He had known some addicts in Blanes. But then the piece was written, and I don't know how but it inflated his myth. The people who knew him know that it is nonsense. I think that in *The New York Times* Jonathan Lethem confused it for an essay. It was one of the first important articles on Bolaño and it kickstarted the story. It was not in the interest of the publisher to negate it, because it created an aura.

PIEL DIVINA, on the phone from Fontainebleau, France
In attitude towards life and literature, Roberto could be comparable to a Beat artist. This was the point of the Infrarealists. We were not sponsored by any sacred cow of Literature and we were totally self-taught. Before being the revered writer he is today, Roberto did a lot of miserable little jobs. In Mexico City we lived on a minimal budget. But he was not a Beat in the sense of being an alcoholic. He was a very serious writer, dedicated to his work. He was never a drinker, he always had tea instead. He didn't take seriously that gospel that claims that Beatniks have to get high and drink. He was a sort of scribe of two Beatnik groups, observing them from a distance. The rest of us were more destroyers, we liked getting to the bottom of things. We could get very drunk if necessary. This legend of Bolaño as an alcoholic or drug-addicted writer is just an invention for commercial reasons. Roberto was always on the sidelines—he had to be—for he was the scribe of the time and he gave his testimony of the time.

BRUNO MONTANÉ, Bar Cèntric, Carrer de les Ramelleres, Barcelona

There is something fundamental for me in his writing, his capacity for fabulation, his desire to tell, which comes from the poem, which always has a narrative core. There are infinite passages in his prose that are absolutely poetic in character. I open a book, read five lines, and identify his style. I think it is absolutely identifiable. But of course, I'm biased, because I was his friend.

ENRIQUE VILA-MATAS, Crep Nova, Carrer del Comte d'Urgell, Barcelona

I would say that Roberto didn't have style. He has a very recognisable prose, but he was not looking for a specific style. It is not what counts in his texts. I think of him mainly as a storyteller. This is one of the reasons why he worked so well in the US, because he returned to narration, the old novel form. Many storylines, characters... As you might know I am not that interested in narration. For example, right now I am reading a lot of essays, things that escape the strictly narrative art, maybe because I feel that at bottom we already know all the stories. That's why I've always preferred Don DeLillo to Philip Roth. But I nonetheless admire Bolaño's almost heroic drive to narrate.

And of course, he is more complex than just that. There is in him the meta-literary thing. There is no doubt that he is a devout Borges-ian. I think it is Borges' influence that makes Bolaño's poetry interesting, among other things. I don't think it is great poetry, but I have found things in it that I like. Not so much because of the quality of the verses but because of what is said in them. In that sense he is like Borges. Borges is an essayist writing poems, which is not ideal; but sometimes the ideas are of such quality that one forgets about the rest. And then he has some images, the evening falling, the colours fading in the patio, which, as images, are beautiful. I think that Borges started by feeling he had to write poetry to become a complete writer. But then he found his way, which was to never write a novel like Tolstoy. He knew he couldn't compete with the great novelists of the nineteenth century, and he knew that their kind of literature was not suited to the century he lived in. Which was a great intuition, because he wrote short stories which are incredibly relevant. Bolaño had read Borges well. It was very important for him. He considered himself from the Borges side, because all writers come from somewhere. He came from Borges. *Nazi Literature In The Americas* comes from Marcel Schwob, who Borges vindicated.

THE INTERVIEWERS

From the centre of Paris we walked along the Seine to the Gare de Lyon. After buying the train tickets, we shared a beer which cost us €10 in a regular bar. On our way to Fontainebleau, the almost-empty train halted suddenly and the lights went out. The loudspeakers warned us that another train had derailed but provided no further information. We looked at each other and decided to search the news to see if we could find out anything about the event. We did not find anything. After nearly an hour, the voice announced that we could proceed. When we checked our mobiles again, we saw that the next French presidential elections were leaning towards the right.

Piel Divina came to meet us at Fontainebleau Station in an old silver Citroën Picasso. He was wearing jeans, leather work boots, and a hat that made him look like a cowboy but which he called 'a tramp's sombrero'. Once in the car we looked at each other and then to him, checking whether his skin was still 'luscious'. The journey to his house took us fifteen minutes in which we barely talked about Bolaño. He told us that the Fontainebleau forest was originally a desert and only after the intervention of Louis XIV—who did not want the sand to reach Paris—was it transformed into a forest.

JOSÉ PEGUERO, at The Sailing Club of Blanes

We were very direct. When Piel Divina arrived in Mexico and did not wait to be introduced or sent a message, he came directly to someone's house. The Infras are like that, and even if they don't write much their work is very much alive and written like we are face to face, talking. We looked for this very lively contact. Some poems can take generations to be understood; there are texts that take years to come to terms with. This is not the case with us, we are not cryptic, it is a language of proximity to the street…

THE INTERVIEWERS

We left the main road and turned onto a dirt path. Before long, we arrived at his house—a low, slim building from the 70s, designed by the father of his wife, Joel. Inside the house, Piel Divina showed us the wooden sculptures that he and his wife make. When we asked him what he was working on currently, he replied: 'In the vacuum. I'm trying to capture the forcefulness of no-space.' He also showed us some books that he had brought from his last trip to Mexico, most of them penned by his Infrarealist friends.

PIEL DIVINA, in the forest at Fontainebleau, France

I was a person with a lot of energy, with a lot of vitality. I had things that Roberto didn't have, so I think that made him notice me.

Bolaño didn't come out of nowhere. He drew on all Latin American literature, which he knew very well. Huidobro, Vallejo, Cortazar... His narratives arose from all he read, though he transformed it all. He read many Latin Americans and the Surrealists in translation, though he never mastered any other language apart from maybe Catalan.

Perhaps Roberto's fame in the United States occurred because he broke from tradition. He was the opposite of a creative-writing-school writer. He escaped from all that. The Infrarealist intention from the beginning was to subvert the entire order of the moment, all the academies, all the dominant programmes. It was an aesthetic challenge that he took to the maximum in his novels.

It's difficult to say if Bolaño is a writer without style. For me Bolaño is a universal writer, neither Chilean nor Spanish nor Catalan. Maybe he went beyond styles, to a sort of neutral zone. He is almost a traditional storyteller. When you pretend to be a universal writer, you erase everything, and perhaps also erase your style. You lose your peculiarities. But, of course, you get other things.

ENRIQUE VILA-MATAS, Crep Nova, Carrer del Comte d'Urgell, Barcelona

But Bolaño cannot be understood only through Borges, because, as I said, he is essentially a narrator. When I wrote *El Viaje Vertical*, a work which won the Romulo Gallegos prize because it was a conventional novel (although exploding from the inside...), the story was of a man in his 50th year of marriage whose wife tells him that she is tired of him. He is on his own with his children, but that is not enough, and so he sets out on a trip in Portugal. Lisboa, Oporto, Madeira. And when I told Bolaño the novel I was writing I said to him, you see, nothing happens. I said that because there was no action, only thought. The narrator was increasingly worried, following his trip. And Bolaño said, 'How come you say that? A thousand things are going on in this book.' He saw narration everywhere; everything was interesting for him. And when he had to read novels for a jury, he said that everything was badly written, but that in itself was super interesting for him, to discover that people had many stories to tell. See, he knew where stories lay.

BRUNO MONTANÉ, Bar Cèntric, Carrer de les Ramelleres, Barcelona

The Bolaño style was crafted more by cynicism than by anyone like the Beats. Cynicism understood as in ancient Greek which means 'dogs'. His style was the style of dogs. Bolaño was interested in the sect of the dog and Diogenes the Cynic and the others. But, as you know, who inspired him a lot was the figure of Archilochus. His poetry must be read, there are many leads there, everything is there.

ENRIQUE VILA-MATAS, Crep Nova, Carrer del Comte d'Urgell, Barcelona

It is true, he had a first epoch where he was quite experimental. *Amberes* is interesting but would have never sold if he did not write the rest. The more commercial things. Commercial not as in 'made to sell', to be sure. It is sometimes said that he quit poetry to make money. But that is not true: he did not sell so much when he was alive. And if selling had have been his goal, he would've probably failed. No, Roberto was very honest with himself. I did love the enthusiasm he expressed when he found an editor. First Seix Barral, for *Nazi Literature in The Americas*. And in fifteen days he wrote *Distant Star* for Anagrama.

PIEL DIVINA, in the forest of Fontainebleau

Roberto had a somewhat ambiguous version of poetry. His poems were descriptive, narrative, cinematic. It was anything but poetic. He drew heavily on poetry, but he did not dare to be a poet. He stopped on the edge of that abyss.

JOSE PEGUERO, at The Sailing Club of Blanes

Roberto was a very political person, but he was not a militant. In Mexico, when you were a foreigner in those years it was difficult to get involved. We were all very close to Trotskyism, which was the purest position you could hold on the Left. But as we say in Mexico, there are only three or maybe five Trotskyists remaining, and they are constantly fighting.

One of the constants of the Infrarealist movement was the affection we had for each other, and the union in the fight we had against established cultural groups. We fought that because it had nothing to do with literature—all the grants, the residencies, the institutional endorsement. You write and you can write a single poem and you can say that you are a poet, without having to appear in institutional lists or anthologies. Poetry, literature should not be about that. There is an obscene need to publish text that is worth nothing but money.

The political programme of the Infras was that of the revolution of the Surrealists. We had a purist position on the Left, but we did not expect to achieve anything; it was idealistic, not militant.

Once, after we were particularly successful in an attack against the literary establishment, we celebrated. Roberto went to the store and bought a small bottle of tequila, and we mixed it with a large bottle of Coca Cola, and we distributed it to each other. Though I think he never drank because he always knew about his liver.

PIEL DIVINA, in the forest of Fontainebleau, France
The Infrarealist poetic movement was not political or ideological. If there was a political commitment from any of the members, they were not representatives of the movement. It was purely an aesthetic and cultural movement. We were coming out of a very hard and cruel historical moment in which several of our peers had decided to join a fight and ended up being killed. The Infrarealist movement was like a desire to survive all that. Roberto was rather apolitical. He was fed by literature and he lived for literature. I do not see him committed to any political attitude. I don't want to say neutral, but apolitical.

JOSÉ PEGUERO, at the Sailing Club of Blanes
The trip that he made to Chile to go to defend the government of Allende— that trip was fantastic because he did it almost all on foot. He was penniless, walking around doing small jobs, looking for the poets in each country he passed through. He told me about the trip in detail. He travelled with some Germans who were cycling all over Latin America. They got on a boat with the Germans, and he said they were amazing, because they were cycling all over the world, despite their very young age. Bolaño's father also confirmed to me that he went to defend Allende.

BRUNO MONTANÉ, La Central del Raval, Carrer d'Elisabets, Barcelona
About Chile. I met him two or three months after his return from Chile. He told me the truth, and be careful, you have to be very careful. The story of memory is constructed each time it is told. Telling things as they happened is not possible. To tell you the truth, I don't remember exactly what he said. The main scene that he told me was that he was linked to a party and they were

waiting for a contact who was going to provide them with weapons to fight Pinochet but that it ended in disappointment.

CARLA RIPPEY, on a Zoom call from Mexico City
He was in Mexico during the coup against Allende, I think. But he had written or talked about going back or being there. I'm pretty sure he was not in Chile when the coup happened. He would have told us, obviously, because we were there and we would have compared notes. So I think a lot of that he kind of elaborated on in his head.

ENRIQUE VILA-MATAS, Crep Nova, Carrer del Comte d'Urgell, Barcelona
Now, about Chile, it is true that he was there. But he did not go there to fight Pinochet, it was accidental. He was there travelling, visiting someone, I think. He was not very politically engaged, although he has been read like that and can be read like that.

PIEL DIVINA, in the forest of Fontainebleau, France
He wrote about Chile and about his participation against Pinochet's coup to enlarge his mythology. If in real life you tell a lie, you become known as a mythomaniac, but if you tell it in literature you are just a fabulator. I don't want to say that Roberto was a liar, but he was an excellent fabulator.

ENRIQUE VILA-MATAS, Crep Nova, Carrer del Comte d'Urgell, Barcelona
With Bolaño's biography there are some fictions that keep repeating, no? Is it not what happens with everyone? There are some clichés that keep coming without remedy. It happens to all of us.

In my case, people always recall that I lived with Marguerite Duras in Paris, something to which I didn't ascribe any importance in the moment that it happened. She was not the writer that she has become today. And I was mostly worried about not paying her. I was quite afraid of her. I lived on the sixth floor and she lived on the third, and every time I went through her door I was afraid she would ask for the money I didn't have. And then the fake interview I did with Marlon Brando for *Fotograma* magazine. I was working for a magazine and I did not want them to know that I could not speak English, so I made everything up.

JOSÉ PEGUERO, at the Sailing Club of Blanes

Even with all his stories and fabrications, he never made us angry. Living with him, the days became long, stretched. We spent hours arguing, talking. Planning attacks on institutions or on the hierarchs of the culture of Mexico. He loved to tell stories, whether they were real or not. His descriptions of Mexico City are very accurate. There are things that he also invented, which is funny because here people have continued to affirm them as they happen in the novel; now over the years they have become historical truths.

Even to this day I think that the fantasies he told us then were much better than the ones that appear in his novels. For example, we were in a café and he said that he lived in the world of the flu, or that he had the flu, and then he started talking as if he was dreaming. He wore winter clothes when it was hot and acted bizarrely with other people. He liked to act like that. Roberto and I always spoke to each other truthfully and always said what we truly believed to one another. Yes, it was an invention. But of course we believed it. That became real and we enjoyed it like little dwarves.

PIEL DIVINA, in the forest of Fontainebleau, France

Fabulating is a part of all the people who live in and for the world of literature because they are creating stories and universes all the time. We used to say to him, 'no mames, párate'. But who are we to criticise or judge? In the end everyone makes up their lives in one way or another. Bolaño, at first, when he was still not famous, did not introduce himself as a poet or a novelist, but as a sculptor, of sculptures of thought. And that is what he did to his life, he treated it like a sculpture.

ENRIQUE VILA-MATAS, Crep Nova, Carrer del Comte d'Urgell, Barcelona

Almost everything I have written is autobiographical but also changed. It responds to a reality, to a truth. In Bolaño this is very evident in *The Savage Detectives*. He is writing about his life in Mexico, but it is at the same time a creation of that life and different from what actually happened. You have the same thing in the birth of the novel, *Don Quixote*. Reality and fiction merge. Reality is there but it cannot fully get into the text. When you are writing you are inventing a mirror whose reflection you will never find. That is the beginning of everything; that's the novel. When people speak of non-fiction I laugh because as soon as we speak, we are always modifying reality, we are performing a literary construction.

dependence on the mean temperature of summer

Nobody knows more closely time's vagaries than Norway.
Glacial epochs sandwiching a warm period resemblant to now
and flora immigrating in the face of ice walls. The strangeness
of Bergen's mostly iceless coast region speared here and there
with cute little glaciers and its Atlantic plant life so much like you:
insular in character. You find yourself moving most in the damp.
On nights when osmosis would only make the air wetter
and your eyes dryer you'll find reproductive prospects in bars
and abstain from taking their hands. Possessions end
up scattered around a bed like they're mourners at your burial.
Asplenium marium. Erica cinerea. Scilla verna. Vicia orobus.
How unethical seeking pain to exonerate your deep
unremarkable. Hunkered down in this erroneous boreal zone
—offered warmth and always recoiling. Seeping wet while outside
cuticle holostea does its celery-convincing boney snaps.

Susannah Dickey

Special Effects

Andrew Meehan

First, we put him on tape. Auditions are embarrassing for everyone, but he did all the expressions I asked for. Not much of a handle on uncertainty but we could have had any amount of disgusted, sad, happy, afraid. I had pangs at his skin alone but it was his lashes that got him the job. We could have stuck falsies on someone, but there's something about a lash that's god given—eyes to send legions into battle, and for putting in a children's film. *Deer Me*. Fawns in love run away from home and pass through misfortune before returning home again.

His agent said that he liked to be taken to all the restaurants; he didn't like to eat he just liked to be taken out. My first mistake was to invite him some place with the faces of actors—old, dead, once famous—lining the wall. Everywhere we looked there was someone better known than him. That will be you one day, I said. Dead? he said. Starters were called for, about seven of them. I was worn out eating off little plates and I was worn out listening to what he'd just been in. He'd been in a play called *Young Neanderthals*, which is why they were certain he'd be a good fawn. He wanted to know where all the food had come from. The horseradish in his Bloody Mary, was it in or out of season? The questions had an actor's lift to them. The intonation was different every time; he had the mastery. We ended the night doing drugs off a wheelie bin, and just to prove that he could play an animal, he tried to bite me.

Good actors find it so easy, as do the bad ones. This is the problem. Stand here, go there, say that. Have a nap, have a wank, complain about the catering, get in the cage, enact violence on a loved one (who will be played by a stranger). That he wouldn't wash his hair and went around dressed like a UPS driver was his own business. When it came to the work he'd cry when I wanted him to laugh, applaud when I wanted him to cry. He was such a total and utter fucking liability—and as lovely as a new pillowcase—that I didn't know what to say to him. A director who doesn't like and can't talk to and is scared of actors is like the fisherman who can't swim—apocryphal but not unheard of—and I had a particular kind of trouble with this one. All he had to do was to stand in front of a green poster and run around like he was a deer. That's easier said than done, he said. But he was a fidgety boy and young deer are skittish, aren't they? He was actually alright at running around. Had we been in a restaurant he might have been able to say the same thing twice, but every time it came for him to speak on set, he just looked surprised.

I had to buy him another dinner. He brought me flowers—lilies, with their fake stink—and I remember that he wore a Hawaiian shirt with matching trousers over unbuckled motorcycle boots. I asked him if the costume department had helped him, he said no. Over thousands of starters, he told me that instead of being an actor he could have been a doctor or a lawyer. Lawyers tend to know their lines, I said. He needed me to convince him that he could be an animal. Wasn't he being paid? I asked.

All the writers and the producers didn't seem to mind that I helped him redo the lines. As long as the boy didn't want a writer's credit. We worked all weekend—at the boy's command and with all the room service he wanted, tray after tray. The advances we made were slow. He saw things I didn't see, questioning things other people wouldn't have. We worked out a backstory for a cute little deer who was suffering from an ancient hurt. I had to remind him that this was a kids' movie. There was, for a fawn, quite a lot going on. He was also a connoisseur of the plot twist—he loved a cheap gag, he'd pour them on like hundreds and thousands; but he had a good ear, and in the end we questioned every last breath and syllable. There was even some nice music to the lines. We played them to a point where he was going to be able to speak the things he had to speak.

The next day we had scheduled an important scene—a tracking shot to rival *A Touch of Evil*, months in the planning. But the breathing exercises he'd been given for his anxiety made him drowsy, and he had to be dragged onto set.

Why he needed breathing exercises for a scene that had no lines in it was anyone's guess. When we were 95 per cent of the way through the shot he got the HICCUPS! I had to break the news to him that he'd ruined the whole thing. Days of work, let's just set fire to a stack of fifties. I got emotional—'A Touch Of Evil!'—and he got emotional, everyone was in a bit of a state. His minder woman was sent for, but one whisper in his ear and the hiccups turned into yelps. I was told he was fine to go on, but the commotion had worn everyone out, and we didn't get the shot. I did invite him for dinner, but they told me he wasn't hungry.

You are a saint aren't you? Some kind of holy man. There you are at the window. You seem to want me to know that you're in the kitchen with your apron on. It's quite something to see a man crouched over a baking tray. It's understood that I don't help around the place. Soup and toast, on occasion. Are you on the phone? What is to be done with Judy, is that what you're saying? She's been like this so long, what can any of us do now?

I've not been very strong on religion for some time now, but I hope you realise that each time I make it as far as our back door, I step onto water; just standing, as you do when you're waiting for a loaf to come out of the oven. And it's not the sea, is it? It's a lawn running with dandelions in need of cutting. If this was one of my films, the lawn would be a sea, and fairies would be dancing on it. The waves, to those in the know, would be hand-drawn, the seams well stitched. I would always do what I could with what I had. All I can say is that I never went out of my way to make a bad film. There wasn't one that I didn't sweat over. How many hours passed in search of a back of hand shot in the right kind of light? And from all that a film appears like a newspaper on a doormat.

The news settled about us as awfully as a plot twist. Of all of them, the death of a young person—someone must have ranked them—is the most hushed and wretched. The boy barely put anyone out; he waited until the second last day of filming, he'd been wrapped, he'd taken his applause, he'd said the nicest of thank yous. All I know of his final agonies was a note that said sorry for not being better. If we could have had a walk together, I would have said that we got through most of the work we had to get through, and not to worry about the mistakes. We'd retrace our steps—the first morning he walked into the studio, and how he wanted to turn around the way he came in. I'd remind him of the scene where he appeared out of the mist—and he'd had to imagine the mist. I'd thank him for placing his trust in me and he would listen to more of the praise that you need when you wonder why you go on and if you are going to. The funeral was a small family thing.

The TV studio reception was the kind of place you'd go to for hiring a van. The programme didn't start until eight, but people were still arriving with toothbrushes on the go, with wet hair. They bundled you off to some room with an urn of tea in it, and a young man, a newsreader of some kind, came to walk me through the segment. He smelled sweet, like a biscuit or a teenager's deodorant. I never could get used to being asked questions about myself (and, of course, it doesn't happen now), but he knew all about what had happened, and he seemed to know all there was to know about *Deer Me*. I asked him what he thought of the film.

—Read the reviews, he said with a pat of his folder.

The special effects, which I didn't understand and had little to do with, were singled out for special praise, and in fact *Deer Me* did very well for something that wasn't very good. Fawns in love are fawns in love, after all, and I had to be mindful of the fact I was there to say nice things about the film. I wasn't there to put people off.

They moved me through to the studio while we were waiting for the news to end. Murder, sport, weather; I knew without having to listen. Then I saw you slip through a door and stand there unobserved by all. (I am always so soothed by your presence that I assume you take comfort in mine.)

The newsreader leant forward to pull up his socks, knee high and thin enough to be expensive. He began by saying, —We have to talk about the fact that *Deer Me* is quite a sad film. Or that it has this sadness attached to it.

On the monitor, I could see the face of the young actor who had died. In a bad film, like the ones I used to make, I would have asked the newsreader for a large brandy. But I said, —I suppose everything is sad if you give it too much thought.

When I dried up, he asked them to play a clip. In the scene, from early in the film, the young animals were being given their mission by the reverend mother. Her words were spoken by a stream busy with insects and frogs that it had taken an age to animate. Everyone could see that the boy's beautiful-boy eyes were dancing with good intent.

—This is such a lovely feat of imagination, the newsreader said.

—Children wouldn't stand for anything less.

—Does it help you stay in touch with your inner child?

—It *might* do.

—What were you like as a child?

I told him that my parents were theoretical physicists and that I was a theoretical person. If there was insect within reach, it got experimented on. I had a cardboard box full of baby mice. For my experiments. I was a little girl who wanted the world to be happy. But I wanted the mice to be happy too. I sang them to sleep, I was a giver of lullabies to mice. I got sick, too, not the mice's fault, but I got sick anyway and I ended up spending a lot of time alone. I was a busy little child, always busy, sad, and bored.

—Friends?

The newsreader seemed to want to know if I had had any friends!

—They considered putting me in quarantine. There was a mark on the wall, a patch of damp on a wall, and I'd talk to the damp-patch. His name was Mark, named for a mark on the wall.

That made him laugh, so I wasn't about to say that one day I had a party and filled all the cups in my tea-set with bleach. I think the smell was the give-away. They caught me with the cup an inch from my mouth.

—I was always a worry to my parents, I said.

—They eff you up, your mum and dad?

—I don't really think so.

There was more that I didn't say to the newsreader. One day they found me on a chair on the lawn. There was a Bic pen strapped to my hand. I was getting a grip on things, see! I was drawing cartoon clouds, and soon I was drawing pictures of rain. I drew the drizzle, I threw the pen in the air and I drew that. Puddle suds and drops on webs. If you're the way I am, people say you can't help yourself, but this misses the point. You can try. I sat drawing in that chair until they moved me inside, where I drew clouds from memory. (They were very good clouds. I'd like you to find me a better cloud.) Then I took a chance on drawing the things I couldn't see. I drew the fire in a room I'd never been in, I drew the cold in my bedroom, I drew the dusk, I drew the scraping in the wall.

That's when I started taking photographs. Photographs of nothing, much like people take today. My meals, my shins. Later I found other ways to try. All the lovey-dovey stuff keeps you going. Straight-laced lovers, lovers who loved me.

Accountants aren't supposed to be clairvoyant, but I'll never forget how quickly you responded to my message. I wasn't good on the phone, and that only seemed to draw you in more. You said it wasn't that far to walk from your office to mine, but I know how long it took to walk from town and it didn't look like you'd taken any buses. You were sopping in a suit of brown wool that's still hanging in your wardrobe. You did me the courtesy of not being disgusted by the mess—I wasn't about to tell you I had been fired by my cleaner—and I paid you the compliment of pretending not to notice how you came alive in the details. All my receipts were in shoeboxes and you went through them with a bird's eye for danger. Not a drop of judgement in you either when I told you what couldn't be accounted for: island-hopping, the best heroin, all of this on cash borrowed from a matt-black credit card.

In a day or two of phone calls, we had established that you were appalled by me, and that I was pleased to meet someone who was appalled by me. It was either that or the fact that you got my accounts in order, and so on. It was a question of finding the right medicine.

(Please note that I am not saying that you are like medicine.)

It was becoming clear that I wasn't morning show material. The newsreader was disappointed with my answers. He asked me if I'd anything else in the pipeline. I said there was a time when I was full of ideas, they came as easily as they went, but one good way to ruin an idea was to turn it into a film.

I got up the courage to ask for a sip of water. With the glass at my mouth, from the door behind you came the creature with his fawn tail bobbing.

He had a message for me: he was sorry for not saying his goodbyes. Was there sorrow in his eyes? Yes, there was—and mercy, far too much of it for one so young. The days were a little long, he said, they had their own shape. But that was how he liked it, no annoyance from anyone. He wanted me to know that the berries and nuts and leaves you find to eat in the woods were a gift from heaven. As long as there was a stream to drink from. Once, he'd stolen some oats from a sack but oats were no more than porridge and he'd chew the bark off a tree if he had to.

I told the newsreader that was that. Could they stop the show, or could I go? I could see you there now, in the studio, by the exit. The squeal of a mic and the look on your face. You could have hidden the panic. But you got all the wires off me and pulled me up out of my seat.

You had my hand and we were walking. I tripped over some wires, I've no idea what it was like underfoot for a fawn. He moved as quickly as I felt I was moving slowly. I had no notion that I had done this to him; I had put a boy's head on a deer's body, and he was trotting behind us—I could feel him—and you were pulling me with you, harder than I was happy with. It became a race through the studio corridors with the creature following. What gets me now is that we were so rude to run away. I could see that in his eyes, he was wondering why we were getting into the car in such a hurry. I wanted him to come with us, I wanted to take him home.

I'll be here as long as I can last, or until you come out and get me. This lawn? Your Christmas cakes are firmer. It's not a garden at all it's a marsh, a war film, one of mine. Fix bayonets, get them one in the eye. Sometimes the things you're not supposed to think of as beautiful are the most beautiful of all. This morning you blew on my forehead. Were you getting rid of a cobweb? You stood over me, and it was strange to feel your breath on me. You're in dire need of a seeing to, but don't be complaining to me, I haven't let you go without. I prefer the mornings that begin with a whistle. Two notes, and the way in which this begins as a kind of reflex—and the gentle way with which you use it to wake me every morning—strikes me as only one kindness of many. No matter what lovely things happen later, the silence of morning will be the kindest thing you do. Other than those two notes, you don't say a word, you don't make a sound. That's another thing; if you mind the quiet, I would never know. I think of this all the time, not that you are ever being impatient or short with me, but on account of your kindness, and how I will never get to the bottom of it.

There was an entire city out of the window of that car, a river, and the creature was going to help us fly over it. He was out there on his own, running as fast as the car, he was really keeping up. I asked you to get the driver to stop, but you said we had to get back to the hotel. It didn't matter that the boy was at the window. I was trying to roll the glass down, but he was all alone on the busy road, I was trying to help him climb in the window—'come on then!'— and I loved the very sight of him struggling, and he could barely manage it. I was close enough to see his lashes and wipe his face; there was fur on it, the special effects really were very realistic. And I was so scared that we were going to run him over. I was trying to help, he was begging me to help, and he was starting to cry. But how was it that he could be running behind the car and then in front of it? I wanted to attach a rope to him. What if we got him to pull the car along like it was a sleigh? We would fly through the city behind him, the creature pulling so hard that the driver would lose control, and I was losing control now, and letting go of you already.

There's a peeled orange and someone has been kind enough to tap the top of my egg—'shall I set the table?'—and I eat everything you have made for me—'tap tap'—and afterwards there is lunch on my face and you wipe it off.

I must have dreamed again. You were walking away from me up the garden, your big long legs kicking at the dandelions. I must do something today. Sometimes I don't want to get out of bed, or I haven't wanted to go to sleep. I know that every time I fall asleep you'll worry if I'll wake up in one piece.

You've run my bath, but the water's too hot, and I have to stand in it until it cools. I can hear you being quiet. There'll be a towel slipped onto a hook and you can interpret my mood from the how I slip it off. I have my bath and I do my skin things. A gallon of water and a good night's sleep, massage yourself into putty: this is the secret to good skin. But getting older isn't so much coming apart as not being whole, never having been that way, and not knowing what I would do if I was. And, if we're going out, I'll need you out of the way so I can use the sink alone. But you are alongside me in the mirror, drying your hair, or brushing it, or playing about so you can be next to me, or keep an eye on me. Even in a mirror, you can get in the way.

You're rooting in your ears with a cotton bud (you'll poke a hole in your own head one day). I catch you holding the dirty end up to the light.

—We haven't really gone out much this year, you say.

—There's time yet. It's only November.

—Perhaps we should go somewhere today?

—I need hand cream. I'm getting old woman's hands.

You stick your hair under my nose. If we're going out today, I want to wear something nice. But the holes in my ears are so rarely used that I have to apply force to get in the studs. I can feel it happening sometimes, but I'm not ready to slip away. I don't want to go anywhere, and I don't want you to either. If there's one thing I know—'sniff my hair'—is that when we're apart we're useless.

—Do people get weird when you say you're married to me?

—It doesn't come up much in Tesco.

—What do you say you do? When people ask you.

—No one asks me.

Can we watch something when we get home from the pharmacy?

I am always changed by the creature's presence, and grateful for his reappearance—grateful, yes, to be alive and to have survived, and that this is a memory, a story I'll tell. He took the trouble to appear and once should have been enough. But you need to know that it's the creature who chooses when to appear, and each time he does, for some stupid reason, the hiccups still won't stop. Drink a glass of water upside down, I say. Tilt your head, listen more intently, listen, and remember that you don't know the ending, just play the scene you're in. But the quality of the picture deteriorates—clouds drift to a halt, the SFX get worse and worse, the sound is unfinished and the grading is poor. There are faces missing, limbs missing. This is not post-production work to be proud of. Nor does this boy know that I'm sorry, and how sorry I am. So, I keep him in sight, asking for direction, and speaking to me in lines that I once gave him, in language that I taught him and only we could understand, and that I have long forgotten.

The Blackhills

Eamon McGuinness

Pat Rathigan left Skerries at 23.50. A group of men tried to hail him at the edge of town but he ignored them, double-checked the light on his roof sign was off and picked up speed as he drove the coast road towards Balbriggan. The Irish Sea was quiet, the moon high and bright.

He pulled into the small layby at the Lady's Stairs, the sea hidden by large trees. Reversing and parking next to the bottle bank, he kept the road in his sights then took out a yellow microfibre cloth from the glove compartment and wiped down the dash, metre and ID. He left the key in the ignition and his door ajar, and shivered when the cold air hit him before taking a deep breath through his nose. From the boot he took a cardboard box of empties, all rinsed: vodka, beer and wine bottles, two jars of sauce and a small bottle of Calpol. He looked around after each drop, winced at the sound of the glass echoing in the quiet night, then put the box back in the boot.

The odd car went by. Pat kept an eye on the road, checked the time on his phone and opened the back-passenger door. It was five minutes after midnight. He walked to the base of the Stairs. The gate was locked, but easily hoppable, the streetlight beside it a harsh orange. He blinked hard and looked down the overgrown path leading to Barnageera Beach and whistled twice. He heard rustling, then a return whistle. He rushed back to the car and started the engine. A few seconds later, Mick Rathigan scuttled across the tarmac, head low. He dove into the back seat and pulled the door closed as Pat spun left out of the layby, taking the first right under the railway bridge.

—You're a lifesaver, Pat, a fucking lifesaver.

Mick reached through the front seats and grabbed Pat's left arm.

—Alright, Mick, alright. Lie down.

—I won't forget this.

—You're shivering.

—It was fucking freezing down there.

—There's a blanket and some food beside you.

—Thanks, Pat. I haven't eaten all day.

Pat beeped at the bends as the road wound up towards the Blackhills, while Mick scoffed the roll and bag of King crisps.

—Which way are we going?

—Through the hills. Stay down.

—Let me know where we are.

—Climbing now. Ardgillan coming up.

—Nice one.

—Did you manage to sleep?

—I drifted off but was too nervous. I got a bit of shelter in the old changing spot.

—Was there anyone about?

—A couple of people walking dogs and one swimmer, but I was well hid.

—I can hear your teeth chattering.

—I'll be grand once I warm up.

—I'm taking the left here at Ardgillan.

Pat turned up the heat and put the foot down on the straight stretch of road as they passed the new cricket club on the right.

—No Elvis, Pat?

—Not tonight, I can't enjoy him in this mood.

—Fair enough.

Passing St Mobhi's graveyard, Pat blessed himself, reduced his speed, dropped to third gear and glanced at Mick over his left shoulder, who was lying flat on his back, his legs twisted down behind Pat's seat. They made quick eye contact before Pat refocused on the road.

—Passing Milverton now.

—We're flying.

At the T junction Pat turned right onto the Skerries Road.

—How's everything at home? Mick asked.

Pat looked in the rearview mirror but couldn't see any trace of Mick.

—Grand, given the circumstances.

—Has Lilian been sleeping through the night?

—Don't talk about Lilian, Mick.

—Fair enough. I was just asking.

Pat ran his left hand through his thick white beard and opened his window to let in some air.

—Does Lorcan know about this? Mick asked.

—No one knows and I plan to keep it that way.

—What did Butsy say?

—He has it sorted.

—I knew he was the man to ring.

—The ferry's at four from Belfast. You'll get to Cairnryan at seven and should be in Inverness by lunchtime.

—Amazing, he has a bed and all in the truck.

—I know.

Pat coughed hard a few times and closed the window. They were on the road to Lusk and passed the new estates on the left.

—He's a dodgy fucker, but he's always been a mate. Remember what he was like in his twenties?

—Don't, Mick.

—What?

—I'm not in the mood for *remember when*. We're coming into Lusk, stay down.

—Anyone about?

—A few stragglers.

—I always thought Lusk was a kip.

The lights at Murray's Lounge took an age. Pat kept looking from left to right, scratching his beard while they waited.

—Here we go, at fucking last.

—Many Gardaí around tonight, Pat?

—A few more than usual.

—Did you pass the house?

—A couple of times, yeah.

—And?

—There's tape still around the gate.

—Was there anyone outside?

—No, the place looked dead.

They were out of Lusk and on the old Dublin Road, passing farms and glasshouses.

—Where are we, Pat?

—Nearing the turn for the estuary.

—I shat myself every time I heard a siren.

—What did you do with your phone?

—I fucked it in the sea after I rang you. If they trace the calls, they'll think I drowned myself.

—Did you call Mam?

—No, she wouldn't understand. If they question you, just tell them I was saying goodbye.

—Grand. We're getting a good run at it now, coming up to Blake's Cross.

—I'll miss it round here.

—I don't wanna hear it, Mick.

—I appreciate what you're doing for me, Pat, I really do.

—I just wanna get you out of this car.

Pat took a left at Blake's Cross. There was a little traffic on the R132, the road dotted with factories, warehouses and garages. He opened his window and changed to fifth gear for the first time.

—Have you heard anything about Sara? Mick asked after a long silence.

—Yeah, I was in with her earlier.

—Where is she?

—Beaumont.

—And?

—She's in a bad way, Mick. A bad fucking way.

—Has she talked yet?

—The Guards are waiting for her to come around.

—I fucked up.

—You fucked up?

—Yeah, I fucked up.

—Fucked up? Fucked up? Pat screamed.

—Alright, Pat, calm down.

He slowed the car, dropped to fourth gear and looked back at Mick.

—Fuck off, Mick, it's barbaric what you did to that girl.

—Okay, it's just—

—Don't try to explain yourself.

—Watch the road, Pat.

A car beeped and overtook them. Pat regained his composure and looked forward again.

—You did that to your own daughter. What sort of fucking animal are you?

Pat hocked and spat out the window.

After a long silence, Mick spoke.

—Where are we, Pat?

—Turvey, swinging left. Two minutes.

—My heart's beating out of my chest.

—This is it for us, Mick, I'm telling you. Don't contact me again.

—What about Mam?

—Leave Mam to me.

Just off the main road, Pat indicated left into a house. A man with an Alsatian on a leash was at the gate and nodded at Pat as he turned in. He brought the car to a stop and the Alsatian barked and jumped at the door.

—Hush, now, good boy, hush.

—All good? Pat asked.

—Grand. You know where you're going?

—Yeah.

—Go on so, Butsy's waiting for ye.

—Good man.

Pat restarted the car and moved down the long, potholed driveway.

—We're here.

Mick sprang up. There were cars on breeze blocks and the garden was full of scrap metal and pallets. Butsy's truck was parked beside the bungalow, its cab blue, with Butler Transport printed on the side in black lettering. Butsy and another man appeared at the back door of the bungalow and stood under a bare bulb as Pat parked next to a Jeep and trailer. Butsy had a plastic bag in one hand and with the other was holding his Dogo Argentino on a lead. Mick was looking around frantically, his head in-between the two front seats. Taking off his belt, Pat switched on the interior light and faced Mick properly for the first time. He could smell Mick's breath and noticed how filthy and unkempt he was.

—Do you have everything?

—I have fuck all but I have it.

—Good, alright, let's go.

—I'm sorry to ask, Pat, but did you bring that money we talked about?

—Of course.

Pat fiddled in the glove compartment and took out a wad of notes and handed it to Mick.

—I'll pay you back, I promise.

—C'mon, Butsy's waiting.

Mick took the notes with his left hand and with his right grabbed Pat's wrist and planted a kiss on his knuckles. Mick's nails ran along the back of Pat's hand; Pat could feel their length and looked down to see the dirt on his brother's fingers. He pulled his hand away, wiped his knuckle with the sleeve of his jacket and scratched his beard with both sets of nails. Mick stuffed the notes into his right-hand pocket and got out.

Dogs were barking non-stop from behind the bungalow. Butsy called the men over and took a step towards the car.

—I'd say you lads could do with a strong drink, am I right?

—Am I glad to see you, Butsy! Mick called.

Pat closed his door. Mick spat on the ground and began walking towards Butsy. Suddenly, a man appeared from the darkness on Pat's left and swung a bat cleanly and swiftly at Mick's head. He fell instantly and the man gave one more solid strike to the back of Mick's skull. Butsy and the other man were running and before Pat had moved, they had Mick bound and gagged and were lifting his body away. The Dogo Argentino growled at Mick before Butsy quietened it with a few strokes to the head. Pat opened the car, took out Mick's blanket and dropped it on the ground. One of the men had a grip under Mick's armpits and the other was holding his ankles, the body floppy and loose. Pat fished into Mick's pocket and retrieved his money.

—Go on, Butsy said to the lads.

Butsy put his hand out and Pat shook it. Together they watched the two men carry Mick towards the sheds at the back of the property. Butsy got on his hunkers and scratched his dog behind the ears, then stood up, interlaced his fingers and cracked his knuckles.

—Scumbag. He won't be missed, Butsy said.

Pat was staring at the ground, shaking his head.

—Fucking savage.

—How's Sara?

—Bad, Butsy, bad. He perforated her bowel. She's having colostomy surgery in the morning.

—He's a fucking animal. Don't worry, he'll be disappeared within the hour.

—I don't wanna know, Butsy.

—It's over, Pat, you've done your bit. Will you come in for a drink?

—Not tonight. I should get going, I've to swing by the Ma's.

—Fair enough, we'll sort him out, then I'll hit the road myself.

—Is it an overnight?

—No, I'm back here later. It'll be a long day.

—For sure.

—How are the roads?

—Dead, not a crisp bag blowing out there.

Butsy smiled.

—January, what?

Pat nodded and kicked the blanket.

—Would your dogs sleep on this? He was lying under it in the backseat.

—I'll burn the fucker.

—Thanks, Butsy.

—It's nothing, Pat. Give the car a decent scrub in the morning.

—I'll bring it in for a valet.

—Good idea.

Butsy raised his hand for a high shake and Pat took it, and Butsy then placed his left hand on Pat's shoulder for a couple of seconds.

When he was settled back into the car, Butsy knocked on the window and Pat rolled it down.

—Are Lorcan and his family still living with you, Pat?

—Yeah, the lot of them are in the spare room.

—How old is the granddaughter now?

—She'll be six months in March.

—If you ever want a pup for her just let me know. No charge, chipped and all.

—Nice one, Butsy.

—I've always got a couple of pregnant bitches about to drop.

—Thanks, I'll say it to Lorcan and Elaine.

Butsy nodded.

—A bit late to be going to your Ma's, no?

—Blocked sink. I told her I'd sort it. She hardly sleeps that woman.

—Sinks are a pain in the hole. Tell her I was asking for her.

—Will do.

—Go on, Pat, I'll be in touch.

—Thanks, Butsy.

*

The man and the Alsatian were still at the gate when Pat swung right out of Butsy's and drove towards Blake's Cross. Mick's smell was in the car so he kept the windows open. The roads were almost empty. He gripped the steering wheel with both hands and kept his eyes forward. Before he hit the Five Roads, he turned for the Man O'War. He passed the GAA club, Oberstown Detention Centre and the pub, took a right at Kennedy's Corner, the left turn at Killary Grove, right again onto Darcystown Road then onto Baltrasna and the second left into his mother's cottage in the Blackhills.

Using the torch light on his phone, he checked the inside of the car. On the backseat was the clingfilm from Mick's roll and the bag of crisps. He shook the crumbs and few remaining crisps onto the grass and stuffed the rubbish into his back pocket. He found a bit of bread on the floor. There was no ham or cheese left, just a crust with a thick spread of butter. He walked to the ditch at the side of the cottage and threw in the bread. He looked around, unzipped, and pissed into the brambles and bushes, then wiped his hands on his pants. From the boot he took out a mini hoover. It made a low whining sound as he went over the seats and floor thoroughly. He sucked up gravel, sand and crumbs from Mick's food. *Filthy prick*, he muttered to himself. He emptied the hoover into the ditch and returned it to the car. He sprayed some air freshener, left the windows open and locked the doors.

The sensor light came on outside the back door. He knocked twice before unlocking and entering the cottage. His mother was lying the full length of the couch in the kitchen-cum-living area, the radio blasting near her head, the fire fading. She looked to be sleeping but her head shot up when Pat entered. Without saying anything, he filled and turned on the kettle. He grabbed two eggs from the fridge and put them in a saucepan. She was taking her time to sit up, yawning and stretching, as Pat leaned over her to turn off the radio.

—Any news, Pat?

—No, nothing.

—What about on the phone?

—I haven't heard anything, Mam.

—What time is it?

—Nearly one.

—Many out there?

—Very quiet. An airport run delayed me.

—Grand.

—Are you hungry?

—No, I had a sandwich a while ago.

He put some kindling and a briquette on the fire, took her plate and cup from the coffee table and left them on the counter.

—I'd say he's long gone at this stage.

—Who knows, Mam?

—I just have a feeling.

—We'll see.

—Did you dump the bottles?

—I did.

Pat checked the sink. It had been spat in; grey, green and speckled with blood. He put on a pair of rubber gloves, lifted the bucket of bleach, stepped into the garden and poured it down the drain at the side of the cottage. There was a frost in the air. He picked out the S trap and ran cold water through it from the outside tap. Under the sensor light, he poked around the pipe with his fingers, removing grease, eggshell, potato peel and rasher fat. When he came back in, he put the empty bucket underneath the glug hole and ran the tap. The water ran through the spit and he had to rub with his baby finger until it dislodged. He looked over to his mother. She was watching him work.

Outside again, he emptied the bucket on the grass, then went and filled the saucepan with the boiled water and set a ten-minute alarm. He fiddled around with the pipes under the sink and got the S trap back on, tightening and securing it.

—Is it fixed, Pat?

—We'll know tomorrow. I got a fair bit of gunk out of it.

He poured water from the kettle slowly down the sink. There was a gurgling sound and some spurted back up before disappearing.

—I'll be back tomorrow to check it.

—Ok. Will you bring Lilian with you?

—Of course.

—Your sister rang.

—What did she say?

—Sara is in a bad way.

—I know, she has surgery in the morning.

—Nine o'clock, Deirdre says.

—That's right.

She started to weep and blew her nose into a hankie. The eggs were tapping off the side of the saucepan. He checked the time on his phone. From the press he took out vinegar and baking soda and added them to the glug hole before pouring in a bit more water.

—Mam, don't put anything down here and please spit in the toilet or on the grass.

—It's the dentures, Pat.

—I know, but I'm the one has to fix it. Just throw the food into the garden.

—I don't like encouraging those birds.

—Well, in the bin then, but not down the sink, please.

He checked the time again and reduced the heat.

—Has Mick been in touch?

—He rang and tried to talk but I hung up.

—The Guards will be on to you.

—Why?

—Ye are brothers.

—They'll be on to all of us so.

—Did you not notice anything?

—I knew it was an unhappy house. We all knew that.

—He's lost his way since Margaret died.

—He never had a way, Mam. There are no excuses.

—I'm not excusing him, Pat. I'm just trying to understand.

—I'm finished with him.

—It's different for me. They'll destroy him inside.

—They'd put him with his own, they always keep the pervs together.

—Don't call him that, she wailed.

—Okay, Mam, okay, calm down.

His phone beeped. He turned off the eggs and poured the boiling water slowly into the sink. It flowed smoothly down the glug hole. He refilled the saucepan with cold water then placed his two hands on the counter, dropped his head and stared at his shoes.

—Go home, son, you're dead on your feet.

—We should have protected that girl more.

—You can't save people, son.

—She's your granddaughter, my niece.

—We're on our own out there, you should know that by now.

—Maybe. Maybe not.

—He'll be out in a few years. If they catch him.

—I don't know, Mam. I'll peel these and head off.

—Thanks, son.

—You go to bed. Do you want anything on?

—Mendelssohn.

She had her own route around the cottage and he didn't offer any help. She gripped the arm of the couch and from there grabbed her walking stick and clung to the radiator and then the door handle. He stayed behind her in the hall and guided her to the edge of the bed until she flopped inside. He put on the CD.

—My purse, Pat.

He found her purse under the cushion on the couch and handed it to her in bed.

—There, Mam, all sorted.

—When are you going to shave?

—Soon. I haven't had time to bless myself this week.

—It makes you look old.

—I am old.

—You know what I mean.

—Good night, Mam.

He did a quick clean-up of the living room, peeled the eggs and put them on a plate in the fridge. He set the coffee table for the morning and refilled the kettle, dropping a tea bag into her cup. He emptied his back pockets and held Mick's clingfilm and crisp packet in his hand. He opened the hall door and listened. He couldn't hear his mother but Mendelssohn was clear. Throwing Mick's rubbish on the fire, he watched as it crinkled and burned. He put on the fire guard, tapped his jacket for his keys and looked around. He called goodbye but she didn't answer, then turned off the lights and locked the door behind him.

Instead of taking the direct route to Rush, Pat went right towards Balrothery and into Balbriggan. He didn't switch on the radio or any music. The streets were empty as he turned right at the hotel, crossed over the train tracks and picked up speed once the town was behind him and the coast road opened up. The Lady's Stairs and layby were empty. There was little wind and the Irish Sea was dark and still, the lights of Skerries Harbour visible in the distance. A blue flashing light hit him as he took the last bend into the town. He bit his bottom lip, slowed down and scratched his beard. A florescent yellow and blue Garda Jeep was parked in the middle of the road and two guards in full uniform were chatting outside their vehicle. He didn't recognise either man.

The guard on Pat's side put his palm out and the car was brought to a stop. Pat's knees shook as he wound down the window. The guard nodded at Pat, took out his torch and scanned the car's tax, insurance and NCT. The guard's breath was visible in the air as he leaned down to speak.

—How's it going?

—Grand, guard, just heading home.

—Where's home?

—Rush.

—Are you local?

—All my life.

—What's the name?

—Patrick Rathigan.

—Many out?

—No. A few airport pickups but very quiet.

A car pulled up behind Pat and the guard gestured for it to stop.

—Okay, can I see your taxi licence?

—No bother.

Pat removed his Driver ID from the dash and handed it over. The guard checked the details and registration plate. He took another look at the licence before handing it back. There were two cars backed up behind Pat now.

—Okay, safe home.

—Thanks, guard, have a good night.

Pat left the window down and drove off. Stopped at traffic lights in Skerries, he exhaled deeply and took a second to compose himself. He put the foot down when the lights changed and met only one car on the road to Rush. A group of lads tried to hail him outside The Yacht Bar but he increased his speed and arrived home in ten minutes. He checked the time—01:42—then put his phone on airplane mode.

He sat in the car for a few minutes until his heart rate settled. The houses in the estate, lit by the orange street lights, looked small and shabby. The green in the centre of the estate was patchy and wouldn't be cut now till February at the earliest.

He went in through the side door, his hand shaking as he fiddled with the keys. As he walked, the sensor light came on and he stood on the patio, watching the end of the garden. The light went off then on again then off and he unbuckled his belt and loosened the top buttons of his shirt. He looked at the spot the fox had been digging every night and pissed on it.

*

In the extension, Pat kicked off his shoes and left them by the door, slid out of his belt, then took off his socks and threw them in the direction of the washing machine. His phone torch navigated him through the debris of toys and baby paraphernalia. He switched on a lamp and the cabinet lights, then lit a single candle and placed it in the centre of the island. He turned on the heat for an hour and put on the kettle. At the bottom of the stairs, he stopped to listen to the house. In the front room, he turned on the lamp in the corner then looked at the street and his car. Nobody passed. He removed his jeans and shirt and put on his house pants, T-shirt and jumper, which he'd left on the couch. He turned on the TV and muted the sound straight away. He pressed play on the DVD and while it was loading went back to the kitchen and made a pot of tea, leaving two bags in the water. He collected all his clothes and put them in the washing machine, added a few more from the basket and left it ready for the morning. The time on the cooker was 01:56.

Pat cleaned his hands and face in the jacks, filled his nostrils with water then blew hard into the sink. He hocked out some phlegm and spat a few times into the toilet. Back in the kitchen, he added milk to a cup, grabbed the pot and brought them to the windowsill in the front room. He stacked two cushions at the end of the couch and laid out a blanket. The curtains were open and through the mirror above the fireplace the reflection of the streetlight could be seen. He skipped some scenes till he was where he'd left off the previous night. He unmuted the sound and set the volume to three. In black, with a high collar and open-necked shirt and surrounded by four musicians wearing red, Elvis sang 'Lawdy Miss Clawdy' in the round. Scotty Moore was to his immediate left. The faces of the people in the crowd could be seen clearly. Pat smiled and nodded along. He poured his tea and stretched out on the couch, but halfway through the song he heard his granddaughter crying upstairs and the eventual shuffling of feet. The cries got steadily louder and the movements more frantic.

Pat climbed the stairs, knocked on the bedroom door and waited on the landing. Lorcan came out.

—Howaya Da?

—Here, I'll take her, son.

—I think it's the teeth.

—C'mon, I'm off tomorrow, get a few more hours.

—Are you sure?

—C'mon.

Pat followed Lorcan into the bedroom. A lamp was on in the corner and Elaine was propped up on pillows trying to calm Lilian.

—Elaine, love, I'll take her.

—It's not fair on you, Pat.

—It's fine, I won't sleep for a while yet. G'wan, get a couple of hours.

Elaine held out Lilian and he took her in his arms.

—Are you just in, Da? Lorcan asked.

—Yeah.

—How was it?

—Dead, a few stragglers but nothing going.

—Any news about Mick?

Pat glanced at both of them but fixed his eyes on Lilian.

—No, nothing. Yous go back to sleep, I'll sort this one out.

—Thanks, Da.

—Yeah, thanks, Pat, you're a lifesaver.

—I'll chat to yis in the morning.

Lilian whimpered and jiggled in his arms until he got his grip right and she settled, but he felt something off with her. In the kitchen he switched on the warmer and popped in a bottle from the fridge. He tried not to talk or make eye contact with her, but she was fully awake and pawing at his face. While the bottle was warming up, he changed her on the floor. The nappy was dry, but she had a bad rash. He wiped her carefully, removing some lint from her belly button, and applied cream. With another wipe he cleaned in-between her fingers and toes, behind her ears, mouth and nose. Her nails were long and jaggedy and she had a few light scratches on her face. She didn't like her nose being touched but he held her head as she squirmed and got rid of the dry snots. She cried a little, a sort of heavy wail, but he gave her a plastic toy and she brought it to her teeth. Leaving her on the mat then, he filled a syringe with Calpol and took the bottle off the heat. He checked the time again: 02:17. She hadn't moved from the changing mat but was attempting to flip over. He took the dodo out of her mouth and with two shots gave her the full 5mg.

In the front room, he propped her up on the cushion with her head raised and fed her the bottle. She drank half in frantic gulps and he put the dodo back in. He sat her forward and rubbed her back until she let out a strong burp. He skipped back on the DVD, pressed play and kept the volume low. Her eyes fixed on the screen. Pat gently sang 'Are You Lonesome Tonight?' to her. She squirmed a little so he returned the bottle to her mouth. She took another 20ml then drifted off to sleep without being burped. He placed his baby finger in her palm and she instinctively made a fist around it. He stayed like this for a few minutes watching Elvis. His tea was lukewarm, and he drank two cups in a row. He leaned close to her and kissed her on the forehead. Her head was tilted slightly to the left. He picked up his phone and was about to check his messages but instead turned it off completely.

Lilian began snoring, a gentle purr. Pat wrapped her in the blanket and lay her on the floor, surrounded by cushions. He went quickly into the kitchen and grabbed the packet of baby wipes. In the drawer he found the nail clippers, scissors and mirror and returned to the front room. He cut his own nails first. He took his time, stopping to watch Elvis and look at Lilian. When he finished, he cleaned his hands with a wipe then knelt on a cushion, took Lilian's right hand in his and cut each nail with one strong clip, ensuring not to nick the skin. When the hands were finished, he fished her feet out the bottom of her babygrow and did the toenails, then rubbed both hands and feet with a wipe. She squirmed a few times but didn't wake up. He refastened the babygrow and secured her tightly between the cushions. He collected all the nails in his empty cup.

Standing at the door, he watched Elvis. He skipped forward to 'If I Can Dream' and turned it up a little. Elvis was now dressed in a white suit and red tie and sang in front of a giant screen, his name in lights. He was holding the mic in his left hand while his right arm gestured and swayed wildly. Pat noticed the rings on Elvis's fingers. He moved along to the music and when the song finished he shook his head a few times. He repeated the song and while it was playing put the mirror on the couch, knelt down and began trimming his beard. When the song ended again, he restarted the DVD and kept cutting until the black leather of the couch was full of his white hair. He added the trimmings to the cup and poured in the dregs of the teapot. He went into the kitchen, put on the kettle and washed out the pot. He took the cup and rushed out to the garden.

He poured the clippings and trimmings onto the foxhole, running his finger around the inside of the cup to make sure he removed everything. He listened to the house. He could see a lit attic skylight next door. He breathed in through his nose, arched his neck back and looked at the sky, then yawned deeply. The kettle was coming to the boil and blocked out every sound. Suddenly, he dropped the cup on the grass and hurried back to Lilian, leaving the back door open. He found her as secure as he had left her, but she had moved her arms, and they were splayed above her, outstretched. He was panting and took a second to compose himself. Kneeling down, he ran his knuckles along her cheek and listened to her soft breathing. After a few seconds, he went back outside to pick up his cup and lock the back door. He made fresh tea, blew out the candle and switched off all the lights. He left the cup in the front room and crept upstairs. All was still on the landing. He took the duvet and pillow from his bed, brought them downstairs and placed them on the couch. He tucked Lilian in, switched off the lamp, closed the door and drew the curtains fully. The TV screen now illuminated her face, and with a heavy sigh Pat stretched the full length of the couch and let his head drop onto the cool soft pillow.

STINGING FLY PATRONS

Many thanks to:

Susan Armstrong
Maria Behan
Valerie Bistany
Jacqueline Brown
Trish Byrne
Edmond Condon
Evelyn Conlon
Claire Connolly
Kris Deffenbacher
Enrico Del Prete
Andrew Donovan
Stephen Grant
Brendan Hackett
Huang Haisu
Sean Hanrahan
Teresa Harte
Christine Dwyer Hickey
Dennis & Mimi Houlihan
Garry Hynes
Nuala Jackson
Charles Julienne
Jeremy Kavanagh
Jerry Kelleher
Margaret Kelleher
Claire Keogh
Joe Lawlor
Ilana Lifshitz
Lucy Luck
Petra McDonough

Jon McGregor
John McInerney
Maureen McLaughlin
Niall MacMonagle
Finbar McLoughlin
Maggie McLoughlin
Ama, Grace & Fraoch MacSweeney
Paddy & Moira MacSweeney
Lucius Moser
Michael O'Connor
Ed O'Loughlin
Maria Pierce
Peter J. Pitkin
George & Joan Preble
Fiona Ruff
Anne Ryan
Linda Ryan
Ann Seery
Attique Shafiq
Eileen Sheridan
Helena Texier
Olive Towey
John Vaughan
Debbi Voisey
Therese Walsh
Ruth Webster
The Moderate Review
Museum of Literature Ireland
Solas Nua

*We'd also like to thank those individuals who have expressed the preference
to remain anonymous.*

BECOME A PATRON ONLINE AT STINGINGFLY.ORG

*We extend our sympathies to the family and friends of Paddy MacSweeney, a long-time patron
and enthusiastic supporter of the magazine, who along with his wife Moira has been a very
welcome presence at many of our events down through the years. Ar dheis Dé go raibh a anam.*

NOTES ON CONTRIBUTORS

Anonymous has been published in *The Stinging Fly* and elsewhere.

Marie-Helene Bertino is the author of the novels *Parakeet* and *2 a.m. at The Cat's Pajamas,* and the story collection *Safe as Houses.* Her work has received The O. Henry Prize, The Pushcart Prize, and The Frank O'Connor International Short Story Fellowship. Her alien opus novel *Beautyland* is forthcoming from FSG.

Gary Boyd is a writer based in Dublin. He published an essay in the second issue of *The Stinging Fly.*

Lorie Broumand is a librarian. Her stories have appeared in a handful of places, including *Confrontation, SmokeLong Quarterly, Vol. 1 Brooklyn, Memorious, The Cafe Irreal, Burning House Press, Litro,* and *Fiction Southeast.* She's writing a novel about a milkman.

Lucy Sweeney Byrne is a writer of short stories, essays, reviews and poetry. She is currently working on a novel.

Joshua Calladine-Jones is a poet and the literary-critic-in-residence at Festival spisovatelů Praha. His work has appeared in a number of journals, including *3:AM, The Anarchist Library, Minor Literature[s],* and *Literárni.cz.* His pamphlet, *Constructions [Konstrukce],* was published with tall-lighthouse in 2021.

Patrick Deeley's seventh collection with Dedalus Press, *The End of the World,* was shortlisted for The Farmgate Café National Poetry Award. His poems have appeared in many leading journals worldwide over the past forty years and he is a recipient of the Dermot Healy Prize and The Lawrence O'Shaughnessy Award.

Susannah Dickey is a writer from Derry. Her most recent pamphlet is *bloodthirsty for marriage* (Bad Betty Press, 2020) which received an Eric Gregory Award from The Society of Authors. Her first novel is *Tennis Lessons* (Doubleday UK, 2020).

Clodagh Beresford Dunne's poem 'Seven Sugar Cubes' won The Irish Book Awards Irish Poem of the Year (2017). She is a recipient of an Arts Council of Ireland Emerging Writer Award. In 2019 Edna O'Brien DBE bestowed Beresford Dunne with the UK's Clarissa Luard Award for Emerging Writers. Her debut collection has just been completed.

Phoebe Eccles has been published by *Ambit, SPAM zine, Strix Leeds, (RE) An Ideas Journal* and *SOFT EIS,* and her work is featured in the anthology *Love Spells & Rituals for Another World.* She is currently studying Creative Writing (MLitt) at the University of Glasgow.

Wendy Erskine lives in Belfast. Her first collection, *Sweet Home*, was published by The Stinging Fly Press in 2018 and Picador in 2019. Her next one, *Dance Move*, will be out with The Stinging Fly Press and Picador in February 2022.

Maria FitzGerald writes about identity, motherhood, love, loss and our interactions with nature and place. She holds a first-class BA (Hons) English & Geography from UCC, where she was College Scholar in 2017. She is a recipient of a Poetry Ireland New Poet Bursary (2021/2022). She lives in Lismore, Waterford.

Seán Golden was born Irish in London. Childhood in Ballina and Ballaghaderreen. School in the USA. Returned to Ireland. Some years in China, many in Spain. Published in *Cyphers, The Crane Bag, The Field Day Anthology of Irish Writing, The Drumlin, Force 10, The SHOp* as well as *The Stinging Fly*.

Sarah Maria Griffin is from Dublin. Her most recent novel is *Other Words For Smoke*, and she tweets @griffski.

Rebecca Ivory lives in Dublin and writes short fiction. Her stories have appeared in *The Stinging Fly, Banshee, The Tangerine* and *Fallow Media*.

Jessica Gaitán Johannesson is a Swedish/Colombian writer and climate justice activist based in Edinburgh. Her debut novel *How We Are Translated* (Scribe), published in 2021, was longlisted for The Desmond Elliott Prize. She is *Wasafiri Magazine*'s Writer-in-Residence 2021-22 and works as Digital Campaigns Manager for Lighthouse Books, Edinburgh's radical bookshop.

John Kinsella's most recent volumes of poetry include *Drowning in Wheat: Selected Poems 1980-2015* (Picador, 2016), *Insomnia* (Picador, 2019) and *Brimstone: a book of villanelles* (Arc, 2020).

Yang Lian is a Professor of Poetry at the European Graduate School EGS and an influential contemporary poet. He was one of the Misty Poets, an underground group of Chinese poets surrounding the literary magazine *Jintian* (*Today*). He won the 2021 Sarah McGuire Prize for Poetry in Translation.

Emer Lyons is a lesbian writer from West Cork living in New Zealand. She is the postdoctoral fellow in Irish Studies at the Centre for Irish and Scottish Studies. Most recently, her writing can be found at *The Pantograph Punch, Newsroom, Queer Love: An Anthology of Irish Fiction*, and *Landfall*.

Seán Lysaght is the author of six volumes of poetry, including *Scarecrow* (1998), *The Mouth of a River* (2007) and *Carnival Masks* (2014), all published by The Gallery Press. His *Selected Poems* appeared in 2010. He has also written prose about wildlife and landscapes in *Eagle Country* (2018) and *Wild Nephin* (2020). He lives in Westport, County Mayo.

Liz MacBride is a writer from Kildare. Her fiction has been published in *Sonder Magazine* and the Epoque Press e-zine. She is currently studying for a PhD in Literary Practice at Trinity College Dublin.

Eoin Mc Evoy is a poet, translator and artist who works through Irish. He was selected for Poetry Ireland Introductions 2021 and has had work published in *Comhar, Feasta* and *Green Carnations*. He is a past winner of the REIC and Craobh Aimhirgin poetry competitions and co-founded the collective AerachAiteachGaelach.

Jon McGregor is the author of five novels and two story collections; his most recent novel is *Lean Fall Stand* (4th Estate). He is Professor of Creative Writing at the University of Nottingham, where he edits *The Letters Page*, a literary journal in letters. He lives in Nottingham, England.

Eamon McGuinness' fiction has appeared in *The Stinging Fly* and *The Lonely Crowd*. He has won the Michael McLaverty, Wild Atlantic Words and Maria Edgeworth short story competitions. He holds an MA in Creative Writing from U.C.D. His debut poetry collection, *The Wrong Heroes*, was published this year by Salmon Poetry.

Scott McKendry was the recipient of the Patrick Kavanagh Poetry Award 2019 and his pamphlet, *Curfuffle* (The Lifeboat), was Poetry Book Society Autumn Choice 2019. He's currently working on his first full collection.

Andrew Meehan is the author of the novels *One Star Awake* and *The Mystery of Love*. His third novel, *Instant Fires*, will be published by New Island Books in autumn 2022.

Jacinta Mulders' writing has been published widely, including, most recently, in *The Believer*. She completed her MA in Creative Writing (Prose Fiction) at the University of East Anglia. She currently lives in Bandar Seri Begawan, Brunei.

Aaron Obedkoff is a writer and student based in Tiohtià:ke (Montreal). His work has been featured, or will be forthcoming, in *O:BOD Magazine* and *Arc Poetry Magazine*.

Ilse Pedler's pamphlet, *The Dogs That Chase Bicycle Wheels*, won the 2015 Mslexia Pamphlet competition. Her first collection, *Auscultation*, was published by Seren in 2021. She is the poet-in-residence at Sidmouth Folk Festival and works as a veterinary surgeon in Kendal. www.ilsepedler.com

Michael Phoenix is a writer and researcher from Belfast. His work has been published in *The Stinging Fly, The Dublin Review, Channel* and other journals. He is working on a novel.

Billy Ramsell's most recent collection, *The Architect's Dream of Winter*, was published by Dedalus Press in 2013. Over the years he has published poems, articles and translations in *The Stinging Fly* and was a guest editor on Issue 32 of the magazine.

Maurice Scully, born 1952, is the author of a dozen plus books, most recently *Humming* (2009), *Several Dances* (2014), *Play Book* (2019) and *Things That Happen* (2021). A new book is forthcoming from Shearsman in 2022. A collection of essays on his work, *A Line of Tiny Zeros in the Fabric*, appeared in 2020.

Stephen Sexton is the author of the books of poetry: *If All the World and Love Were Young* (Penguin 2019) and *Cheryl's Destinies* (Penguin 2021). He teaches at the Seamus Heaney Centre, Queen's University, Belfast.

Maria Sledmere lives in Glasgow. She's editor-in-chief of SPAM Press and a member of A+E Collective. An exhibition, *The Palace of Humming Trees*, with Katie O'Grady and Jack O'Flynn, was recently shown at French Street Studios. Her debut collection, *The Luna Erratum*, is out now with Dostoyevsky Wannabe.

Patrick Stasny is a writer and translator who lives in London. He has published on fashion, literature and music. He is currently working on his first novel.

Jim Toal lives in south Shropshire, UK. His fiction has been published in literary magazines such as *Litro, The Mechanics Institute Review, The Forge Literary Magazine,* and *Shooter Literary Magazine*. He is currently working on his first short story collection. You can contact him on Twitter @jtstories.

Jessica Traynor's debut poetry collection, *Liffey Swim* (Dedalus Press, 2014), was shortlisted for the Strong/Shine Award. *The Quick* was a 2019 Irish Times poetry choice. Residencies include the Yeats Society Sligo, The Seamus Heaney Home Place and Dún Laoghaire-Rathdown. *Pit Lullabies* will be published by Bloodaxe Books in March 2022.

Jodie Wray lives in Belfast. This is her first published story.

Frank Wynne is an Irish literary translator from French and Spanish whose authors have included Michel Houellebecq, Javier Cercas and Virginie Despentes. He jointly won the DUBLIN Literary Award, and has twice won both the Scott Moncrieff Prize and the Premio Valle Inclán. He edited the anthologies *Found in Translation* (2018) and *QUEER: LGBT writing from Ancient Times to Yesterday* (2021). He is collaborating with *The Stinging Fly* as our first translator-in-residence and is chair of the 2022 Booker International Jury.

Hyam Yared is a Lebanese poet and novelist who writes in French and Lebanese Arabic. Born in Beirut in 1975, her first collection of poetry *Reflets de Lune* (2001) was followed by her first novel, *L'Armoire des ombres*, in 2006. Her most recent, *Implosions*, was published in 2021. She is the founder and president of Centre PEN Liban, the Lebanese chapter of PEN.